CW01011339

THE ORRELL COALFIELD, LANCASHIRE, 1740-1850

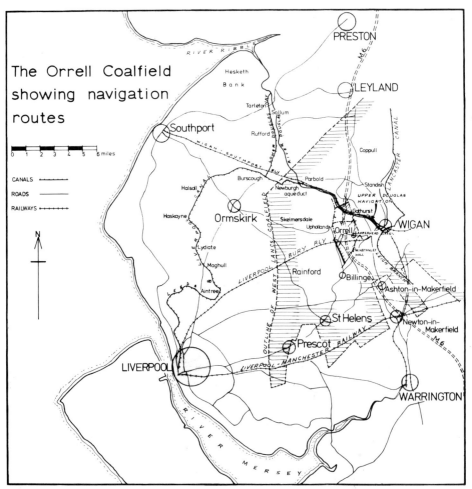

The Orrell Coalfield showing navigation routes

PRESTON

LEYLAND

RIVER RIBBLE

Hesketh
Bank

Tarleton

Sollum

Southport

Rufford

WIGAN SOUTHPORT RLY

Coppull

CANALS
ROADS
RAILWAYS

Burscough

Parbold

Standish

Halsall

Newburgh
aqueduct

UPPER DOUGLAS
NAVIGATION

Ormskirk

Skelmersdale

Haskayne

Upholland

Orrell

WIGAN

N

Lydiate

Maghull

BURY RLY

Rainford

LAMPERHEAD

WINSTANLEY
HALL

Billinge

Aintree

OUTLINE OF WEST LANCS COALFIELD

Ashton-in-Makerfield

LIVERPOOL & BURY RLY

St Helens

Newton-in-
Makerfield

M6

Prescot

LIVERPOOL & MANCHESTER RAILWAY

LIVERPOOL

WARRINGTON

RIVER MERSEY

0 1 2 3 4 5 6 miles

Plan of the Orrell Coalfield showing navigation routes

The Orrell Coalfield, Lancashire 1740-1850

D. Anderson

MOORLAND PUBLISHING COMPANY

To the memory of my father, James Anderson 1882 - 1971, who in 1896 was bound apprentice to Jonathan Blundell & Son and for many years held important positions at their collieries. His detailed knowledge of those collieries was unrivalled and of great use to me in the writing of this and other articles, even though I myself served my apprenticeship there.

ISBN 0 903485 23 0

Typeset by
ARTEC GRAPHIC SERVICES LIMITED
London and Stafford

Printed in Great Britain by
WOOD MITCHELL Ltd., Stoke-on-Trent

for the publishers
MOORLAND PUBLISHING COMPANY
The Market Place, Hartington,
Buxton, Derbyshire, SK17 0AL

Contents

Illustrations

ACKNOWLEDGEMENTS

The author wishes to acknowledge the help generously given him in the preparation of this book by Mrs J.H.M. Bankes of Winstanley who read the proofs and who also helped as an historian in many other ways; Professor T.C. Barker and Mr Iain Williamson who also read the proofs and suggested improvements; Mr James Parkinson of Pemberton who made the fine sketches of work in Blundells' Engine Pit at the time he was a carpenter and pitman there, under my father; Mr Richard Stanton of Orrell whose great store of knowledge of the locality and its people was extremely useful; Mr Eric Ridgeway and Mr David Dalton of the NCB; Mr Gershom Knight, the Wigan Borough Archivist; and the County Archivist and his staff at Preston.

CHAPTER ONE

The Historical Background

1.1 INTRODUCTION

The motorist travelling north along the M6 Motorway from Warrington will pass the No 25 slip road to the A49 for Wigan South. One and a quarter miles north of this, he will pass under a road bridge which carries the A571 from Wigan to St Helens and a mile further on in Winstanley Hall Park he will cross the Tinkerhole Fault into the Orrell Coalfield, which is the subject of this study. The M6 runs through the middle of this coalfield like a spine. Continuing north for three and a half miles to a point just beyond the Gathurst Viaduct over the Douglas Valley, the motorist will pass over the outcrop of the deepest seam worked and out of our coalfield.

This coalfield is a small part of the great Wigan Coalfield, although for some fifty years after the opening in 1774 of the Leeds and Liverpool canal, which cuts through the northern end of it, it was one of the two most important coal producing areas of the Wigan district, the other being the famous Haigh-Aspull cannel area. Its maximum extent was 3¾ miles from north to south and 1¾ miles from east to west. As will be seen later the number of workable seams was not to be compared with that of the central part of the Wigan Coalfield, where there are eighteen.

The Orrell Coalfield lies west of Wigan, the eastern edge of it (the nearest to Wigan) being only just over two miles from the town centre. The coal in this field underlies practically the whole of the township of Orrell, one third of the township of Winstanley and small areas of Pemberton, UpHolland, Shevington and Billinge.

Parts of the district, notably the Winstanley park and Dean Wood—Gathurst areas, are quite picturesque, while other parts are rather bare and treeless. The ground rises gradually from 60ft OD in the Douglas Valley near the northern end of the coalfield to 400ft OD at the extreme southern end. The land continues to rise from here for three quarters of a mile to Billinge Hill nearly 600ft above sea level, crowned by its ancient beacon and surrounded by sandstone quarries once famous for millstones and grindstones. This high ridge formed by Old Lawrence Rock and Dyneley Knoll Flags, runs parallel to and three quarters of a mile west of the western edge of our coalfield for two miles. Huge

extensive underground slate- and flagstone quarries worked from
shafts and inclines from the late eighteenth century up to the
late nineteenth century are to be found in this ridge. The great
cavernous workings 25ft high, the roof of which is supported by
stooks about 8ft square, are an awesome sight. Here was produced
the huge flagstones laid round most of Liverpool's public buildings, and those still to be seen at Haigh Hall, some of which are
3yd square, as well as stone slate known as grey slate and used
on all local buildings in those days. The great Roman Catholic
Seminary — St Joseph's College — is a very prominent feature
at the Roby Mill end of the ridge.

Much building has taken place in the central area of the coalfield during the past twenty five years but there is still plenty
of open country at the southern and northern ends. There are
several old and interesting stone farmhouses, notably Ackhurst
Hall and Walthew House on the Pemberton boundary, and Gathurst Fold, Dean House and Knowles' Farm in the Dean Wood
area. Also Orrell Hall in Springs Road, an ancient stone house
altered at various times, and in Orrell Road, Orrell Mount a beautiful Georgian house in ashlar stone built by John Clarke the coal-
owner and now a restaurant; Orrell Lodge, the home of Daglish ⟶now
the engineer is now the Divisional Education Office and the old wish?
parsonage is a very fine Regency-Gothic house. ⟶Demolished

An ancient residence known as Holland House and now a country
club lies near Dean Wood and an important manor house, Winstanley Hall, lies in the middle of its 470 acre park at the southern
end of the coalfield. Professor Nikolaus Pevsner in his series *The
Buildings of England* says 'in the County by far the best Eliza-
bethan survival is the triplet of houses near Wigan: Bispham Hall,
Orrell of 1573, Birchley Hall, Billinge of 1594 and Winstanley
Hall of before 1596'. Subsequent research has shown that the
latter was built in about 1560. Gregson in his *Portfolio of Fragments* published in 1817, comments that Winstanley Hall

> is pleasantly situated on the edge of a hill commanding a distant view
> of Wigan, Haigh Hall, Rivington Pike and a range of Yorkshire hills....
> not far hence are two chapels under Wigan, Billinge and Holland. Bill-
> inge is about one mile and a half south of the Hall; and Holland church
> or priory the same distance north west. Vast quantities of coal are
> raised in this district which is very populous....and most excellent nails
> hinges screws etc. are made in this neighbourhood where there are also
> many cotton weavers.

Regarding the agriculture of the district, the soil of Winstanley
is described as 'sandy mixed with clay in places with sandstone
rock not far from the surface'. That of Orrell is described as 'clay

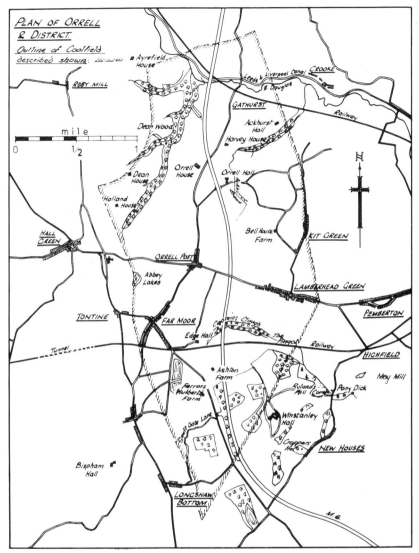

1 Plan of Orrell and district

with a mixture of sand over a foundation of hard stone'. *(VCH of Lancs,* 1911, **4**, 87, 89). The Winstanley estate accounts show that the crops grown during our period were potatoes, oats, wheat, barley, clover, beans, peas and turnips. Potatoes, turnips and clover seem to have been introduced at Winstanley during the second half of the eighteenth century. A survey of Winstanley estate farms in Orrell and Winstanley in 1833-4 gives oats, potatoes, hay and wheat as the principal crops. A considerable acreage was pasture and meadowland. Many copses, small woods and thick hedges are mentioned which must have given the area a pretty appearance: 'the hedges are well adapted for game....fences well adapted for game, an old pit in the middle wants levelling or planting, the stream at the bottom is supposed to have trout in it'.

The relative importance of Orrell in the Wigan coalfield at the beginning of the nineteenth century is indicated in *Pigot's Commercial Directory for Wigan and District* of 1816. Ten colliery concerns are listed, five of which are in Orrell itself and one in Pemberton.

Although Gregson states that the district was populous in 1817, it was not thickly populated by modern standards. For instance, in 1801 at the height of coal production, the population of Orrell was 1,883 for an area of 1,542 acres. It only rose by 769 during the next half century when all the principal collieries had finished. The population of Winstanley scattered over 1,852 acres was 631 in 1801. It rose to a maximum of 800 in 1821 but fell to 675 in 1851. It appears to have been a very static community for in 1901 the census returns show only 564 inhabitants in Winstanley.

Regarding Pemberton, UpHolland, Billinge and Shevington, small portions of which were in our coalfield, during the years 1801-51 the population of the first doubled itself, the second increased by one third, Billinge increased by one third and that of Shevington almost doubled.

This coalfield was probably unique in Lancashire in being so geologically favourable for exploitation by the relatively primitive techniques of the period preceeding its virtual exhaustion about the middle of the nineteenth century.

It was a coalfield which had been worked from at least the commencement of the sixteenth century by small groups of pits (vertical shafts) and day eyes (horizontal adits), mostly in the Dean Wood and Red Wood or Captain's Clough areas. The late Earl of Crawford once stated that cannel was worked by his ancestors, the Bradshaighs, at Haigh, four miles away, from the beginning of the fourteenth century and therefore local people were no strangers to the art of mining in those early days. It was however, the advent of inland waterways, beginning with the completion of the River Douglas Navigation from the Ribble Estuary to Wigan in 1742, that brought about the great development of this coalfield, which was worked so intensively that it was, for all practical purposes, exhausted before the coming of the railway in 1848 (from Bury to Liverpool) and 1855 (from Wigan to Burscough). After the opening of the Leeds and Liverpool Canal to Dean Locks in 1774, Liverpool and Bradford merchants, who had become aware of the profit potential, moved in to exploit the field by taking out leases of coal (chiefly the deeper and unworked Orrell Four Feet Seam) and by buying coal estates. Certainly from this time and perhaps earlier, much of the driving force was coming from Liverpool, just as Liverpool men were behind the opening up of the St Helens coalfield and the construction of the Sankey Canal in the 1750s, so here again in the 1770s they seem to have been repeating the process. Previously a considerable amount of the Orrell coals sent down the Douglas Navigation had been shipped to the Fylde district and other areas in North Lancashire, although some had gone southward round the coast to Liverpool.

Liverpool, soon to become one of the greatest cities in England was growing very rapidly. Its corporation pursued a very enlightened policy and this was said to be one of the chief sources of the town's prosperity. By the middle of the eighteenth century, it was already the equal of Bristol in imports and exports of merchandise and engaged extensively in the highly profitable slave trade from Africa to the West Indies and the American plantations.

Liverpool, during the latter part of the eighteenth century, was hungry for coal, both for domestic use and for its rapidly expanding industries, such as brewing, distilling, salt boiling, sugar baking, iron founding and its associated small scale engineering industry, copper smelting, glass making and potteries — Liverpool being famous at that time for its Delft ware. Cargoes of coal were also shipped round the coast to other towns or across the sea to Ireland. Apart from the shipments of coal to Ireland the Orrell coalmasters supplied a regional market unlike their contemporaries on Tyneside whose market was more on a national scale, London being one of the chief consumers of Tyne coal.

To put the Orrell coalfield in perspective, during the 1790s the output approached its near maximum of 250,000 tons having increased sixfold in the previous twenty years. This was more than a third of that for the whole of the South West Lancashire coalfield which Langton estimates at 700,000 tons. Nef gives the following annual estimate for other coalfields during the same period:

Cumberland	500,000 tons
Ayrshire	162,000 tons
Fife	250,000 tons
Lanarkshire	500,000 — 600,000 tons
Somerset	140,000 tons
Forest of Dean	94,000 tons

These figures show that Orrell was not an insignificant coalfield. Nef's figure for the whole country is 10 million tons, 3 million tons of which were produced in the great Durham and Northumberland coalfields.

In about 1790, soon after the opening up of the deeper Four Foot Seam at Orrell, a great step forward took place in the method of working when it became the practice to completely extract the pillars formed in the seam during the first working. Instead of a loss of 40 per cent of the coal in the abandoned pillars as had previously been the case, only about 10 per cent was lost.

The period covered by this study was a time of great change in the living and working conditions of the miners and indeed of the labouring classes generally and this is considered in a later chapter.

1.2 GEOLOGICAL STRUCTURE

The Orrell coalfield (Fig 1) is bounded on the south-east by the Tinker Hole Fault which has a maximum throw of 185yd down south-east at Winstanley Hall, and trends in a north-east direction from the Billinge Chapel End of Longshaw Common, along Park Road and under Winstanley Hall to Leader Street at Lamberhead Green, where it joins the Great Pemberton or Highfield Fault and its accompanying shatter belt. This trends in a direction slightly west of north from Tanpits, under Highfield Secondary School, Leader Street, City Road Kitt Green and onwards under the Manor House and Ackhurst Hall to Greaves Wood at Gathurst. It has a downthrow to the east varying between 400 and 500yd.

The western edge of the area is the outcrop of the Orrell Four Feet Seam, which starts at the southern end from the Tinker Hole Fault at Chair Wood near Longshaw and trends slightly west of north along the brook dividing Winstanley and Billinge, and on through the east end of Tracks Lane, across to St James' RC Church. From there it continues to a point where it is thrown out by an upthrow fault just east of Tontine Methodist Chapel. This fault displaces the outcrop back to the Abbey Fishpond south of Abbey Lakes Hotel. From here it carries on in a straight line west of Holland House to a point 150yd north-west of Rothwell House, where it is thrown out by the Grand Dyke Fault, a 40yd upthrow to the north. From there the field is bounded by a fault branching off the Grand Dyke and trending north under Dean House and on to Green Alley Wood, east of Ayrefield House. The northern limit

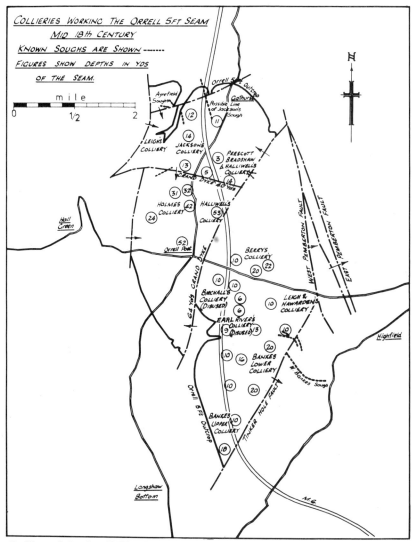

Colleries Working the Orrell 5ft Seam
Mid 18th Century
Known Soughs are Shown -------
Figures Show Depths in Yds
of the Seam.

mile
0   1/2   2

Ayre field Sough
Orrell S. Outcrop
Gathurst
Possible Line
of Jackson's
Sough
12
11
14
Leighs Colliery
Jacksons Colliery
Prescott Bradshaw & Halliwells Colliery
3
3
5
4
Grand Dyke 40 Yds.
31
32
Holmes Colliery
42
Halliwells Colliery
53
24
Hall Green
52
Orrell Post
Berrys Colliery
10
20
22
West Pemberton Fault
East Pemberton Fault
10
10
64 Yds Grand Dyke
Birchall's Colliery (Disused)
6
6
Leigh & Hawardens Colliery
10
Earl Rivers Colliery (Disused)
9
3
10
Highfield
10
16
Bankes Lower Colliery
20
Bankes Sough
Orrell 5 Ft Outcrop
10
20
Tinker Hole Fault
Bankes Upper Colliery
10
18
Longshaw Bottom
M.G.

2   Plan of the Orrell Five Feet Seam

of the field is again the outcrop of the Orrell Four Feet Seam, starting at the fault at Green Alley Wood and trending east through Higher Gathurst Farm to Greaves Wood where it is thrown down to the east by the Great Pemberton Fault.

Apart from numerous small faults, two main faults traverse the field. The Orrell Post Fault starts near the eastern end of Tracks

Lane and trends in a north-west direction, extending under the
Makerfield Water Board's reservoir and the Orrell Brick and Tile
Co's kiln, to the fields just west of Edge Hall Lane, where it throws
the measures 192ft down to the west. From there it passes through
Orrell Gardens, along Howards Lane and through Old Fold to a
point on the Orrell Pemberton boundary 100ft south of Porters
Wood where it joins the Great Pemberton Fault. The Grand Dyke
Fault branches off a large fault parallel to and 500ft to the east
of College Road, extends through a spinney 500ft north of Roth-
well House and continues to a point 300ft south of Dean House.
From there it passes through a point 700ft south of Orrell House.
Here it throws the measures 120ft down to the south and extends
to a point 500ft south of Orrell Hall near to its junction with the
Orrell Post Fault.

There are four Orrell seams, the lowest one being the Orrell
Four Feet, from 3ft 3in to 3ft 9in thick, and known elsewhere
in the Lancashire coalfield as the Arley Mine. This coal was sold
as equivalent to the famous Wallsend of Newcastle and 'second
only to the Wigan Cannel, yielding a large quantity of gas, its
slack producing fine coke'. It was exported to New York and elsewhere in the USA in the early nineteenth century. Between 62
and 64yd above this is the Orrell Five Feet Seam, otherwise known
as the 'Smiths coal', described in 1862 by Hull, the geologist as
'the celebrated Orrell Five Foot Seam, long esteemed in the market
but now exhausted over a large extent of country'. The coal was
in two leaves with a total thickness of 4ft 7in to 4ft 10in, separ-
ated by a dirt band of 2in to 6in thick, which varied between 1ft
10in and 2ft 9in from the roof.

Between 13 and 20yd above the Orrell Five Feet is the Bone
or Burgy Mine, a thin seam of indifferent quality. Although this
was never worked during the great days of Orrell, it was worked
sporadically and in small areas by small companies between 1870
and 1930. The principal workings were those of Holt and Scott
from the Burgy pits at the site of the motorway bridge in Moor
Road. They operated from 1872 to 1887 and built a railway to
the sidings at Orrell station. The second largest area of the seam
(about 14 acres), was worked by George Baldwin during 1872-9.
This colliery was situated just northwest of Orrell Post. Another
small colliery known as 'Bold Field' and situated on the north-
east side of Orrell Post worked the Burgy Mine during the same
period.

The Orrell Yard Seam 3ft 6in thick and 58-60yd above the
Five Feet was only present in a small area near Kitt Green and
was worked by Woodcock and Haliburton in the early nineteenth

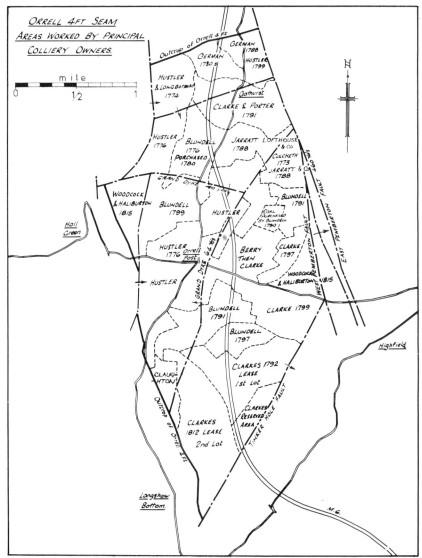

ORRELL 4FT SEAM
AREAS WORKED BY PRINCIPAL
COLLIERY OWNERS.

mile
0   1/2   1

Outcrop of Orrell 4 Ft

GERMAN
1788

GERMAN
1780 S

HUSTLER
1799

HUSTLER
& LONG BOTTOM
1774

Gathurst

CLARKE & PORTER
1791

HUSTLER
1776

BLUNDELL
1776
PURCHASED
1780

JARRATT
1788

LOFTHOUSE
& Co

CULCHETH
1773

JARRATT & Co
1788

GRAND DYKE

BLUNDELL
1791

WOODCOCK
& HALIBURTON
1815

BLUNDELL
1799

HUSTLER

COAL
PURCHASED
BY BLUNDELL
1790

Hall
Green

HUSTLER
1776   Orrell
Post

BERRY
THEN
CLARKE

CLARKE
1797

HUSTLER

GRAND DYKE 64 yds

WOODCOCK
& HALIBURTON 1815

BLUNDELL
1791

CLARKE 1799

BLUNDELL
1797

Highfield

CLARKES 1792
LEASE
1st Lot

CLAUGH-
TON

CLARKES
RESERVED
AREA

CLARKES
1812 LEASE
2nd Lot

Outcrop of Orrell 4 Ft

TIMBER HOLE FAULT

WEST PEMBERTON FAULT

EAST PEMBERTON FAULT

Longshaw
Bottom.

M.C.

3   Plan of the Orrell Four Feet Seam

century, and by Thomas Jenkinson at the junction of Bell Lane
and Latham Lane in the 1860s. Today it is considered an average
quality coal and although sold at Pemberton Colliery in the 1930s
as the 'Arley Yard' it is not in the same class as the Four Feet
and Five Feet, and up to eighty years ago it was reckoned to be
'common coal'. However, we are here only concerned with the

17

Four Feet and Five Feet Orrell Seams. This coal belt must have been a colliery owners' dream, and nowadays it is certain that fortunes could be made out of such a field. No doubt the entrepreneurs of the past made good money out of it! The deepest level of the lower seam was no more than 140·5yd below the surface and correspondingly at its deepest, the upper of the two seams was just over 80yd. Typical sections are shown in Fig 4.

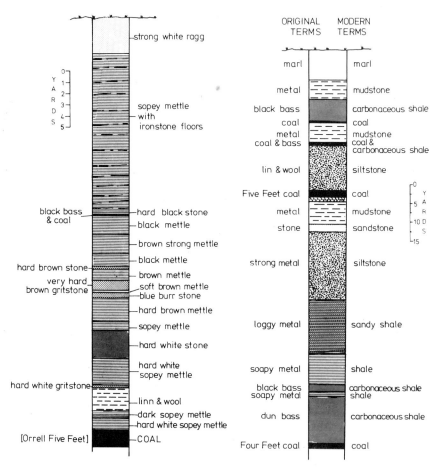

4 Sections of strata. *(left)* Longbothom's borehole at the north end of Dean Wood. *(right)* Hustler's No 17 Pit near Hootons Farm, Orrell Road

Altogether the Orrell-Winstanley field contained just under 20 million tons of the two coals — over 10 million tons of Orrell Four Feet and over 9½ million tons of Orrell Five Feet. Fortunately no less than 6½ million tons of the latter were at a depth of 60ft or under. A very much smaller quantity of Orrell Four Feet, 670,000 tons, lay at less than 60ft.

Thus it was that, except in the Holland House Estate at Up-Holland and north and west of Gathurst Bridge, where the Orrell Four Feet crops out, only the Five Feet Seam was worked (Fig 2) until after the opening of the canal from Liverpool to Dean Locks in 1774. Then there was a 'coal rush', mostly by Liverpool and Bradford merchants connected with the canal, to take up leases of the Orrell Four Feet Seam (and the Orrell Five Feet Seam where it was still intact) from Holt Leigh, William Bankes, Thomas Holme, and owners of smaller estates such as Michael Harvey, who owned 18 Cheshire acres* at the site of the present St John Rigby Sixth Form College (Fig 5).

1.3 OWNERS OF LAND IN THE COALFIELD

No account of mining can be complete without mentioning the landowning class. A glance at any pre-nationalisation Colliery Year Book will show scores of titled company directors. Down the centuries they were vitally concerned with mineral working on their estates, as generally speaking much more money was made from minerals in a far shorter time than from agriculture. Of course coal and all other minerals are a wasting asset, but to the Orrell colliery owner at the time the Douglas Navigation was opened for traffic there must have seemed an inexhaustible supply of coal in the ground.

A brief account of the ancient landowning families of the area is of interest before giving details of the owners of this land during the eighteenth and nineteenth centuries.

The manor of Winstanley, covering the southern end of the Orrell Coalfield, has been in the possession of only two families for at least the past 766 years. It was purchased in 1595 from the original owners — the Winstanleys — by James Bankes, ancestor of the present owner Mrs J.H.M. Bankes, and in his memoranda book James Bankes noted the existence of working coal pits on his newly acquired estate.

---

*The Cheshire acre contains 10,240 sq yd, compared with the statute acre of 4,840 sq yd, and was used for all mining leases in the Wigan area until the Coal Commission took over in 1942.

The manors of Orrell and UpHolland cover all the rest of the field except for the most northern portion in Shevington which belonged to the Standish, Crooke Hall and Holt families and a small area under Lamberhead Green in Pemberton, which before 1760 belonged to Lady Penelope Cholmondley and her ancestors and afterwards to the famous Duke of Bridgewater. These two manors descended in the Holland family who rose from comparative obscurity to become Dukes of Exeter and Earls of Huntingdon. They were soldiers of some repute and one of them, Sir Thomas de Holland, married the Fair Maid of Kent and thus acquired the Earldom of Kent. After Holland's death she married the Black Prince. Sir Thomas, and his brother Sir Robert, were amongst the first twenty-four recipients of the Order of the Garter in 1346. Since then no two brothers except members of the Royal Family have ever held this order simultaneously. Sir Thomas' eldest son, Thomas, was Earl Marshall of England during 1380-5, and was in high favour with his half-brother Richard II. His son, Thomas, was made Duke of Surrey for assisting Richard II, but was beheaded in 1400 for conspiring against Henry IV. Baines, the historian, stated that the last of the Hollands became a fugitive and a beggar in Flanders and his body was found floating in the sea in the Straits of Dover. They have left us a memento in the shape of UpHolland Church which is a relic of the College of Canons founded by them early in the fourteenth century. This later became the last pre-reformation Benedictine monastery in England.

The Hollands had married into the Lovell family and the manors of Orrell and UpHolland were in their possession until the Battle of Bosworth in 1485, when Viscount Lovell, who was on the losing side, was convicted of high treason and was outlawed. After supporting Lambert Simnel's rebellion, he disappeared and a seated skeleton of a man found bricked up in a cellar at his house, Minster Lovell in Oxfordshire, many years afterwards was thought to be his. The two manors along with much other property were granted to Thomas, 1st Earl of Derby, by his stepson Henry VII.

In 1597, William Earl of Derby sold the manor of Orrell to the Orrell family, and they sold it in 1608 to William Bispham of Bispham Hall, Billinge, Alexander Ashurst of Ashurst Hall, Dalton and Alexander Prescott of Ayrefield. Prescott and Ashurst sold their shares to Bispham and it descended with that family until Margaret Bispham, the heiress, married Thomas Owen of The Abbey, UpHolland. They had two daughters, Frances and Mary who married Edward and Holt Leigh, sons of Alexander Leigh of Douglas Navigation fame. The manor of UpHolland was retained by the Stanley family until 1717 when Lady Ashburnham, daughter of the 9th Earl of Derby, sold it to the Ashursts of Ashurst Hall and they in their turn sold it along with Dalton in 1751 to the Bootle-Wilbrahams of Lathom House.

The Priory estate of Holland had included 190 statute acres of land in UpHolland, Orrell and Pemberton. This was purchased by John Holcroft after the dissolution of the monastery in 1534 and later it passed into various hands.

1.4 THE PRINCIPAL MINERAL OWNERS 1740–1850

The Holt family had owned Holt Farm at Shevington for many generations before 1740 and this estate included the north-western portion of the Orrell Four Feet Seam from the outcrop at Gathurst down to the River Douglas. The area was worked by William German during the last quarter of the eighteenth century. George Case of Liverpool having married the heiress of the Holts owned the property in 1830 and bequeathed it to his son Thomas.

The north-eastern end of the same seam (again from the outcrop to the River Douglas) belonged to the Standish family of Standish Hall. This coal was included in a 100 year lease including all the seams under the Standish Estates in Shevington, Standish, Coppull, Duxbury, Worthington, and Wigan, granted in January 1798 to William Hustler, Edmund Peckover and four other Bradford merchants, together with John Lofthouse (a coal merchant from Liverpool) and three local men. This firm constructed the underground branch of the Leeds and Liverpool Canal at Standish Lower Ground.

The Crook Hall Estate owned some coal in the Orrell belt. The estate had belonged to the Catterall family from 1421 until 1713 when Peter Catterall sold it to Edward Holt, who purchased it on behalf of his brother, Robert, who later became one of the undertakers of the Douglas Navigation. In 1724 it passed to their sister Elizabeth Morris, then to her daughter, Anne Pearson, and from her to her daughter Anne Livesey, wife of Robert Livesey. Robert Livesey and his brother, who ran a cotton manufacturing business in Blackburn, failed for nearly £1½ million in 1788. Robert said that they employed 600 looms and 2,400 spinners and were the means of giving bread to 20,000 persons. Their cloth out at bleaching was reputed to stretch for more than twelve miles – a very enterprising business considering it was before the days of factories.

The assignees of Livesey sold Crook in 1789 to Clarke, Roscoe and German, Orrell Colliery proprietors, although it was in the sole possession of John Clarke at his bankruptcy in 1816. It was

then purchased by Joshua Lace of Liverpool, but in the middle of
the nineteenth century belonged to the Woodcock and Eckersley
families.

As far as is known the Leigh family of Ackhurst and Gathurst
Fold Estate, strong in the Roman Catholic faith (some of them
being Jesuit priests) were not related to Alexander Leigh, the Douglas Navigation proprietor. Probably the last in the direct line of
this family was Anne Sandford who, in 1740, gave £100 to the
RC Mission Chapel which her family had founded at Crossbrook
Orrell in 1699 with an obligation for masses to be said for herself,
her mother and two sisters. This chapel was the predecessor of
St James RC Church at Orrell. The estate was sold in about 1770
to William Porter, who, it would appear, had been steward to Sir
Roger Bradshaigh at Haigh. The Gathurst and Ackhurst estates
comprised about 216 statute acres and contained approximately
1,008,000 tons of Orrell Five Feet and 896,000 tons of Orrell
Four Feet, a small area of the seams being thrown out by the
Pemberton Fault.

A small portion of our field was in the Walthew House estate.
This had originally belonged to the Walthew family, one of whom,
Robert, was one of the founders of UpHolland Grammar School,
but it passed to the Percevals in the eighteenth century, and in
the middle of the nineteenth century it was in the possession of
Richard Eccles of Southport, master cotton spinner.

In the early part of our period, Michael Harvey held 15 Cheshire
acres, one rood. This estate was known as the Harvey House Estate
and is the site of the present St John Rigby Sixth Form College.
In the early part of the nineteenth century, it belonged to Ushaw
College, the RC Seminary in Durham, but was purchased by Colonel H.B.H. Blundell in the middle of the century and the house
was rebuilt as the residence of the Blundell Colliery commercial
manager, James Pickering. The Orrell Five Foot Seam contained
232,000 tons and the Orrell Four Feet 171,000 tons.

John Jackson's Orrell House or Salterford estate was sold to
Jonathan Blundell of Liverpool in 1780 on the bankruptcy of
Jackson's son Michael and it continued in the Blundell family until shortly after Major Cuthbert L.B.H. Blundell's death in 1947.
It was 53 Cheshire acres 3 roods in extent and contained 1,425,000
tons of coal — 821,000 tons in the Orrell Five Feet and 604,000
tons in the Orrell Four Feet.

Samuel Prescott had inherited the Orrell Hall estate from his
father Jeffrey and on the former's death in 1756 it passed to his
heirs in joint ownership. They sold it to Holt Leigh, son of Alexander Leigh, in 1769 and after his death it passed to his son Robert

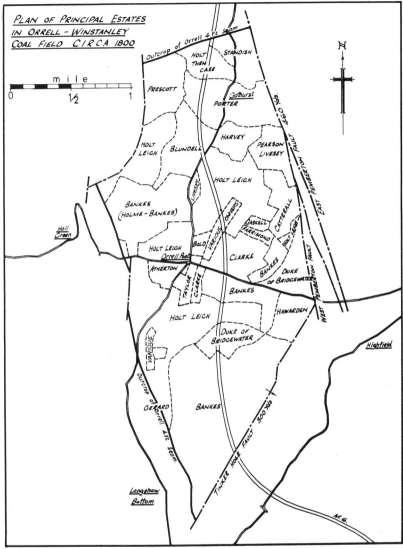

PLAN OF PRINCIPAL ESTATES
IN ORRELL - WINSTANLEY
COAL FIELD CIRCA 1800

mile
0   ½   1

Outcrop of Orrell 4 Ft Seam

HOLT THEN CASE
STANDISH
PRESCOTT
Gathurst
PORTER
HARVEY
HOLT LEIGH
BLUNDELL
PEARSON LIVESEY
LIVESEY
HOLT LEIGH
BANKES (HOLME-BANKES)
GASKELL FARRIMOND
CATTERALL
VARIOUS
ORMROD
HOLT LEIGH
BOLD
CLARKE
Orrell Hall
ATHERTON
TAYLOR CLARKE
BANKES
DUKE OF BRIDGEWATER
Hall Green
BANKES
HOLT LEIGH
HAWARDEN
VARIOUS
DUKE OF BRIDGEWATER
Highfield
GERARD
BANKES
Outcrop of Orrell 2 Ft Seam
Longshaw Bottom
EAST PEMBERTON FAULT 460 Yds
WEST PEMBERTON FAULT
TINKER HOLE FAULT 300 Yds
M.C.

N

5 Plan of the principal estates in the coalfield about 1800

Holt Leigh, MP for Wigan, who was created a Baronet in 1816.
Sir Robert died unmarried in his eighty-first year in 1843, and
his estates passed to his nephew the Rt Hon Thomas Pemberton-
Leigh, Chancellor of the Duchy of Cornwall. The Orrell Hall estate
contained 608,000 tons of Orrell Five Feet and 448,000 tons of
Orrell Four Feet.

Dean House estate in UpHolland had belonged to Josiah Poole of Prescot in the early part of the century, but was in the possession of Alexander Leigh in 1740. He constructed a special branch of the Douglas Navigation at his own expense at the lower end of the Dean Brook so that he could load his coal there. The estate contained approximately 403,000 tons of Orrell Five Feet and 347,000 tons of Orrell Four Feet.

An estate of eighteen Cheshire acres, known as 'Catterall's' at Kitt Green, was purchased from the Bisphams by Taberners in the seventeenth century. The Taberner heiress married into the Catterall family of Crooke Hall. They eventually sold out to Edward Woodcock, who, in 1846 sold it to John Hustler of Orrell Mount and John Mildred Hustler of Orrell Hall.

Holt Leigh owned the minerals under this estate when they were leased in 1791 along with other coal to Blundell and Son. The estate contained 274,000 tons of Orrell Five Feet, 202,000 tons of Orrell Four Feet and an unknown quantity of Orrell Yard near the surface.

Holland House Estate in UpHolland belonged to the Holme family. They had been stewards to the Earl of Derby, and the Stanley crest, the eagle and child, bearing the date 1654 can still be seen on the western gable of Holland House. Hugh Holme had married Anne Bankes, daughter of Thomas Bankes, of Winstanley in 1731. She was sole heiress of her father, brothers and nephew, and the two estates became merged when their son the Rev Thomas Holme succeeded to the Winstanley estate on the death of his cousin, William Bankes, in 1800. The Holme family also owned an estate in Orrell consisting of 54 Cheshire acres 1 rood which contained 805,000 tons of Orrell Five Feet and 609,000 tons of Orrell Four Feet. The Holland House or UpHolland portion of their estate contained 123,000 tons of Orrell Four Feet and a very small tonnage of Orrell Five Feet, as this seam was thrown out by faults.

The Orrell Post House estate belonged to the Berry family during the early part of our period but in the 1790s it was sold by the Trustees of William Berry and Co to John Clarke, Willaim Clarke and William German. German had been raising contractor or manager to the trustees from 1784 and is mentioned in the Land Tax Returns. The estate contained 52½ Cheshire acres, with 800,000 tons of Orrell Five Feet and 590,000 tons of the lower mine.

The Bankes family of Winstanley owned land in Orrell to the north of Edge Hall and in the Oldhams Fold area consisting of 35 Cheshire acres containing 532,000 tons of Orrell Five Feet and 392,000 tons of Orrell Four Feet. In a survey of 1834 Meyrick

Bankes noted that the 'coals are extremely valuable in this estate, but nearly out. Railway and Yorkshire Horse runs through the whole and down to the Liverpool Canal'.

Between Abbey Lakes and Orrell Post on the south side of Orrell Road there was an estate belonging to the Atherton family. Orrell Place, a fine house built by them, contains the following inscription on a central stone in the parapet wall:

Dei: Providentia Hereditas Nostra   (May God
        J & E Atherton 1755   preserve our
        W Atherton Fecit 1820   inheritance)

The estate was only a small one and the coal under it was leased by John Hustler in the latter part of the eighteenth century. The Atherton family had previously owned land north-east of Orrell Post which was acquired by Samuel Bold who was in possession early in the nineteenth century.

Most of the land in the triangle between the fault near Abbey Mill, Orrell Road and Moor Road and a considerable amount on the east side of Moor Road, belonged to the Leigh family who also owned an estate known as Naylor's on the western side of Orrell Post and north of Orrell Road.

Edge Hall estate, part of which is now the site of the Orrell RUFC grounds, was held by Captain Birchall under the Bisphams at the beginning of our period and it was sold in 1789 by Edward Leigh, husband of Frances Bispham, to his brother Holt Leigh. It comprised 40 Cheshire acres and contained 608,000 tons of Orrell Five Feet and 448,000 tons of Orrell Four Feet.

Most of the land under the Orrell portion of Lamberhead Green, between the Great Pemberton Fault and Bankes's Oldham Fold estate, as well as the Duke's Barn Farm estate in Winstanley and the Chapel Street Farm estate in Pemberton north of the Pingot belonged, during the early part of our period, to Lady Penelope Cholmondely. She was descended from the Worsleys of Worsley Mesnes, senior branch of the Worsley family through Roger Downes of Wardley and Richard Savage, Earl Rivers who was her grandfather. Her father was the Earl of Barrymore, one time MP for Wigan, and she married the Hon James Cholmondeley from whom she was eventually divorced. In 1757-9 she disposed of the Lancashire estates which had belonged to her grandfather Earl Rivers. Duke's Barn and the Orrell portion of Lamberhead Green were sold to Francis 3rd Duke of Bridgewater, of canal fame. The Chapel Street Farm estate was sold to Matthew and John Lyon, who soon afterwards sold it to Alexander Leigh. It was eventually purchased by the Bankes family, although Hawarden owned it in 1810. The

Duke's Barn estate originally contained 342,000 tons of Orrell Five Feet and 265,000 tons of Orrell Four Feet.

The most important mineral estate in the Orrell Belt was that of the Bankes family of Winstanley Hall, who owned 1,674 statute acres in Winstanley alone, but the field of Orrell coals we are concerned with came under only a portion of this — about 500 statute acres of Orrell Four Feet and 330 statute acres of Orrell Five Feet. It contained 2,050,000 tons of Orrell Five Feet and a similar tonnage of Orrell Four Feet. William Bankes inherited Winstanley in 1748 from his brother Robert Bankes. He was succeeded by his son William on his death in 1775.

6 Winstanley Hall (from Gregson, *Portfolio of Fragments of the History and Antiquities of Lancashire*)

William Bankes, junior, died in 1800 and was succeeded by his cousin the Rev Thomas Holme of Holland House, who had been curate in charge of UpHolland from 1758 to 1767. Thomas was succeeded in 1803 by his son Meyrick, who, under the terms of the will of William Bankes, assumed the name and arms of Bankes. Although he himself had been educated at Manchester Grammar School of which he was afterwards a governor, he sent his eldest son Meyrick to be educated at Eton and it was during his stay there that Meyrick rented Cromwell House, Old Brompton Road, London. He died there after a long illness in 1827. He was succeeded by his son Meyrick who augmented his possessions in the Wigan area by purchasing the Hawkley Hall and Bispham Hall estates as well as other land. He also bought the vast Letterewe and Gruinard estates in the north-west of Scotland.

The Winstanley estates comprised much coal-bearing land besides the Orrell belt, but this was probably the first worked by the Bankes family, after they purchased the estate in 1595, and it was almost certainly worked by the Winstanleys before them. Thomas Winstanley died in 1561 and in his will he charged his 'coal mynes' with a payment of £20 per annum in the name of his wife's jointure and for the upbringing of her children.

There were quite a number of small estates in the Orrell belt and one of these was that in Billinge Higher End belonging to Sir William Gerard of Garswood New Hall and known as Greenslate Farm, through which the outcrop of the Orrell Four Feet runs.

1.5 THE DOUGLAS NAVIGATION

An Act of Parliament known as *An Act for making the River Douglas alias Asland navigable from the River Ribble to Wigan* was passed by Parliament in 1720, seven years after a similar bill had been rejected by the House of Lords. It had been promoted by local gentlemen interested in the expansion of the coal trade of the Wigan area.

The commissioners appointed under the Act during the period 1720-60 included the following colliery proprietors: William Bispham of Bispham; Thomas Hesketh of Rufford; Jonathan Case of Red Hazels; Peter Bold of Bold; Charles Stanley of Cross Hall; Leigh Master of New Hall, Ashton; Robert Bankes of Winstanley and his brother William Bankes who succeeded him; Sir Roger Bradshaigh of Haigh 3rd Baronet, and after his death in 1747, his son Sir Roger the 4th Baronet; Hugh Holme of Holland House; Thomas Owen of the Abbey; Edward Holt of Wigan and Shevington; Richard Clayton of Adlington.

After the act had been passed there was much delay and lack of interest on the part of those appointed to carry out the work. The construction of the navigation was entrusted to Thomas Steers and William Squire. The latter was a prominent Liverpool merchant. An alderman of the borough, he had been mayor in 1715. Steers, a clever engineer and successful man of business, was a native of Kent. He was brought from London to Liverpool by Richard Norris, Squire's father-in-law and one of the MPs for the borough, to construct a canal to the 'Pool' of Liverpool, but he condemned the scheme and instead constructed Liverpool's first dock which he

opened on 31 August 1715. Previous to this, in 1712, he had surveyed and levelled the River Douglas on behalf of the then pro-
moters. He also constructed the old dry dock in Liverpool, known
later as the Canning Dock, as well as the Salthouse Dock. He was
architect of St George's Church and Liverpool's first theatre and
became mayor in 1739. Regarding the Douglas Navigation, Steers
and Squire were

> to have in perpetuity the benefit thereof with this proviso that they
> should finish it in eleven years after the session of Parliament, which
> if they should not do, any four or more of the commissioners named
> in the Act were authorised to appoint new undertakers. This Act pass-
> ing in the memorable year 1720, the said undertakers sold off in twelve
> hundred shares at 5s. each, one fourth part of the profits of the Naviga-
> tion and to give them credit in Exchange Alley, Mr Steers cut about
> 20 or 30 rods of 8 yards wide and made a little useless lock at the
> lower end of the river, but made no further progress within the said
> term of eleven years.

Steers and Squire were dismissed by the commissioners, who,
in 1733, appointed Alexander Radcliffe and Alexander Leigh to
undertake the work with a similar proviso again that they should
complete it in eleven years. However, little was accomplished until
1738 by which time Robert Holt, Leigh's father-in-law had taken
the place of Radcliffe. That they did finish it within the required
term is proved by a letter written by Alexander Leigh: 'We began
with ye work in ye year 1732 and made a great progress in it but
he [Holt] dying in September 1740 his executors (of whom I am
one) joined with me and finished it in June 1742'. Alexander Leigh
was a remarkable character, who lived at Leigh Place on the north
side of Wigan and was an attorney in the town. He was legal,
business and financial adviser to Sir Roger Bradshaigh 3rd Baronet
of Haigh, who was MP for Wigan for more than fifty years and
many times mayor of the borough. Leigh was also connected with
Sir Roger's fellow MP for Wigan, Earl Barrymore. As a lawyer,
he had a large clientele in Lancashire and in 1733 was steward or
clerk of no less than seventeen manorial courts including Haigh,
Wigan and Knowsley.

Holt and Leigh were constantly consulted by Barrymore on
borough affairs and undertook his disbursements in Wigan. Holt
and his son held the office of mayor on four occasions and Alexander Leigh twice. Leigh was also town clerk from 1732 to 1735
when his son Robert succeeded him in that capacity.

The construction and maintenance of the navigation was fraught
with difficulties and although Thomas Steers had been supplanted,
his expert advice was sought from time to time:

	£	s	d
12th March 1740 Paid Mr Steers for coming over to advise us about the bason and Crooke Lock.	3	3	0
Paid Mr Leigh's bill for Mr Steers charges		18	2
7th July 1742 Paid Mr Stanley's bill of expense on Mr Steers and self when we went to Maels [Meols] to view ye sluice from ye Mear to coast and the next day to Hesketh Bank. Three days and three nights out	1	6	1
4th June 1746 Expenses ye 30th and 31st May and 1st June to meet Mr Steers at Ormskirk going to Tarleton about setting out ye wear	2	12	2
30th July 1745 Paid expenses at Tarleton when Mr Steers came over to view the place for a wear above Becconsall		19	6

Alexander Léigh, the guiding hand behind the whole scheme, was paid 63 guineas a year for his pains. Besides directing the work, he acted as accountant and solicitor to the Navigation:

	£	s	d
9th Dec 1743 For ye accountant's trouble loss of time and expenses (not charged) attending ye work from the beginning 4 years and a half at 63 guineas a year	283	10	0
9th Dec 1743 By Account due to Mr Leigh ye principle undertaker for drawing articles, contracts etc. with masons etc. from ye beginning to ye end of ye work	18	9	0
9th Dec 1743 By account due to Mr Leigh concluding ye design of applying to Parliament for an Act to enlarge ye former powers of ye Act in being	43	8	1

Many cuts were made across meanderings of the river and numerous weirs and locks were constructed. The collective contract seems to have been the system for earth moving and other work. Most of the payments for such work being made to Richard Fell & Co:

	£	s	d
25th Sept 1740 Paid Richard Fell's bill at Dean Lock and Bispham Lock	4	6	0
Paid him more for spade-men at Dean Lock	2	6	0
Gave him to drink		2	6

Fell and his gangs also did other work such as felling timber, cropping fields etc:

	£	s	d
30th May 1741 Paid Richard Fell for work at Apley Lock and in Hulton Park	6	0	0
8th June 1742 Paid Richard Fell at UpHolland Lock and falling timber in Dean Wood	3	6	0
26th Oct 1745 Paid Richard Fell & Co for 2 weeks cropping at Mr Percevals Mr Marklands & Mr Burrows near Waites Delf in Pemberton	3	0	6

Mr Perceval's was Walthew House Estate; Mr Markand's The Meadows, Woodhouse Lane, Wigan; and Waites Delf, near Mr Burrow's land became the site of Pemberton Cottage Hospital.

Much money was spent on timber, especially ash for the weirs and locks and it was felled locally in Shevington, Standish, Parbold, Wrightington, Walthew, Hawkley, Bamfurlong, Hindley, Fairhurst and Harrock woods. Surprisingly, substantial amounts of 'ffirr' were felled at Harrock and twenty-six oak tress containing 440ft felled at Hindley were valued by Fell at £15 2s (£15.10). He carted it to Wigan at the rate of 1¼d per foot. Trees were sawn into planks in a saw pit by two men with a cross-cut saw, one standing on top and one in the pit below. The rate for sawing was 11s (55p) per rood, and a rood for this purpose was 400ft. 'Snigging' was the term used for drawing logs along the ground by horses and ropes after the branches had been lopped off:

	£	s	d
Jan 10th 1749 Paid Mr Molyneaux for snigging wood from ye Dean Wood to Orrell Brow to be carried to Tarleton		5	0

Many boats were built for the navigation proprietors. Names mentioned in the accounts include *Resolution, Despatch, Speedwell, Supply, Success, Assistance, Concorde, Three Sisters, Three Brothers, The Lawrel* and *The Pink*. Not all the boats were built for commerce, as there were two pleasure boats *The Old* and *The New*.

The accounts for building these boats are interesting:

	£	s	d
Paid Mr John Walmsley (by Richard Roper) for a ffir balk 45ft long by 13½ inches contents 56¼ for a kelson (keel) for ye fflatt on ye stocks	3	10	11
6th Dec 1742 Paid Thomas Holland the first of his three payments on account of building the open fflatt on the stocks intended to be called 'The Concorde'	5	13	4

Holland received further payments amounting to £81 9s 9d (£81.49). He went to Liverpool to select a mast, boom, and bowsprit, the expense for himself and horse came to 2s 9d (14p). Planks for boats were bent by steaming, a stove for this purpose being set up at Miry Lane, Wigan.

Bryan Blundell, who founded the Bluecoat Hospital in Liverpool, and whose son and grandson became important colliery owners in Orrell, supplied tar and pitch for the *Concorde* at a cost of £2 12s 2½d (£2.61). This would have been imported from America. Benjamin Robinson, sailmaker of Liverpool, was paid £42 5s 2d (£42.26) for sails for the *Concorde*. Rigging cost £25 2s 9d (£25.14) and ironwork £15 16s 4d (£15.82). Piers Massey was paid 17s 11d (89½p) for painting the vessel and blocks were purchased at a cost of 4s 5d (22p). Other items were:

	£	s	d
Compass		7	10
Pumps	1	5	6
Leathers for the pumps		2	7
Ash for a windlass		10	0
Oars	1	4	0
Tree nails	1	7	7
Small boat [lifeboat] carried by "Concorde"	2	2	0

Large quantities of iron nails were purchased from Chowbent, a noted nailmaking centre. Blankets and rugs were furnished for the cabin.

The launching of the *Concorde* was carried out with due ceremony and true to tradition, as indicated by two items in the accounts:

	£	s	d
11th April 1743 Paid Mrs Buxton for 4 bottles of Rum in punch to the Navigation at the launching of the "Concorde" in June last	1	0	0
Punch from Mr Richard Lees on launching the "Concorde"		10	0

These small vessels sailed out of the Douglas into the open sea and on round the coast, hence the need for compass, masts, sails, pumps, small cock boat etc. The men in charge of them were referred to as masters of the vessels. The quantity of coal carried varied between 34 and 44 tons.

The river was made navigable for the boats by means of locks, weirs and artificial cuts. There were locks at Wigan, Harrison Platt, near Adam Bridge (Wigan), Hell Meadow (Douglas Bank) Crooke, Gathurst, Dean, UpHolland, Appley Bridge, Gillibrand, Chapel House, Newburgh, Bispham, Wanes Blades, Croston Finney, Rufford, Ellerbrook and Tarleton.

After completing the navigation Leigh and the other proprietors had to consider where they could with advantage open up new markets for the coal conveyed down the river. Leigh said:

> The Coal Trade, being the only Article whereupon we depended for a return to answer our expenses (which amounted to £20,000) I considered to what part of ye country it would be proper to apply for ye promotion of it and being informed that Kendall and other parts thereabouts might possibly help in consumption, I went to Millthrop, where Mr Dowkes then my acquaintance recommended to me a house and garden and a small parcel of land called Dixes near Millthrop as a convenient place for a coal yard, whereupon I desired he would purchase it for me.

A sales promotion campaign was launched and in 1748 there were two advertisements in the Kendal press which cost 5s (25p) and '5 several calls by the Bellman' through Kendal cost 1s 8d (8p) or 4d a call.

Although Leigh, in his letter quoted above, states that the navigation cost them £20,000 the accounts give a different figure. Up to 17 December 1743 it had cost £9,866 to make the river navigable, five-sixths of this being borne by Alexander Leigh. The remaining one sixth of the cost was provided by Robert Holt and after he died by his legatees and representatives who were: Henry Holt; Roger Holt; executors of James Holt; Alexander Leigh; Mary Holt; and Mr Chadwick in right of his wife, formerly Miss Holt.

The proprietors took on apprentices from time to time, the first two mentioned were Roger Ashton and Hugh Wood. They were supplied with clothes in March 1742 at a cost of £4 17s 6d (£4.87½). In December of that year, John Molleney was paid £1 1s 6d (£1.7½) for 'making and mending clothes for Roger Ashton and Hugh Wood apprentices to the river'. In 1741 and 1742 the following items were purchased for them:

	£	s	d
two hats		3	0
two pairs of stockings		2	2
eight shirts	1	5	0
five handkerchiefs		4	0

Even their board was paid for when they went home

	£	s	d
16th April 1743 Paid Hugh Wood's mother for his board there 3 weeks when he was not well		9	0

Leigh stated that the coal trade was 'the only article' which they depended on for a return on their capital, but of course other commodities were carried on the river. Apart from coal, the chief goods were limestone and slate from North Lancashire and Westmorland, the coal boats being loaded with this on the return journey. There was also a considerable trade in the local grey slate, flags and paving stones, quarried mainly in the underground delphs at Roby Mill, UpHolland. Mr Chadwick of Birkacre sent quantities of pig iron at regular intervals and other items carried included timber, sand, gravel, bricks, kelp, tow, ox-horns, etc. A maximum toll of 2s 6d (12½p) per ton was fixed by the act for all goods except manure, which was to be carried free of charge to owners of land within five miles of the river. However, agreements for much lower rates were made from time to time. On the 13 April 1754 the proprietors agreed that Ralph Bradshaw of Orrell, yeoman, Thomas Dale of UpHolland, tanner, John Balshaw of Scarisbrick, yeoman, William Kingsley of Wrightington, tanner, and Roger Brandwood of Bolton, gentleman, who proposed to build in partnership 'two flat-bottomed boats or barges to be employed in trade upon the River Douglas', should pay for the term of twenty-one years 1s (5p) per ton 'For the carriage of coal, cannel, limestone, slate, soap, ashes and stone. This is in full payment of all river dues etc'.

From the following notes it is clear that profits were made:

> The last contribution of ye undertakers towards ye general charges of ye Navigation was made ye 28th March 1752. Here ends ye account for ye years 1752 and 1753. The following accounts are to be concluded annually in order to have at ye end of every year (if not oftener) *dividends regularly made*. The year 1753 is included in the accounts delivered to Lord Pollington and Mr Sargeant Poole who purchased each a thirty-sixth share ye 5th February 1753.

The change in the calendar made in 1752 is noted here, as a date is given as '26th ffeb last old style, but 9th March new style'.

After the completion of the Navigation there was much trouble and expense with the locks and banks, and we find items such as the following:

	£	s	d
10th February 1752. Gave John Bibby and James Howard for going down to Crooke two nights in ye rain to draw the clows and paddles and to cut the banks on Shevington side to save the other		3	0
And to drink		1	0

Experts were few and far between, for in October of the previous year Joseph Gilbody was paid 13s (65p) to come from Manchester to Wigan 'to see ye gate which was broken at Appley lock and assist to repair it'. There was trouble again at other places in 1753 when William Bates, mason, was paid 1s (5p) for viewing Appley weir washed down by the floods and going to Wigan to give an account of it. In the following year Hell Meadow weir near Douglas Bank, Wigan, was washed down by floods, and Thomas Ashcroft was paid £2 2s 5d (£2.12) for repairing it.

Thomas Ashcroft and Archibald Mack worked a quarry at Dean and supplied all the stone (dressed or rough) for the locks and weirs of the navigation. Alexander Leigh formed an arm of the river at the lower end of Dean Brook as a private loading wharf for his own coal, and Ashcroft carried out the work there:

	£	s	d
27th May 1748 Paid Thomas Ashcroft & Co for masons work at Dean Brook, but This being at Dean Brook is to be paid by ye accountant as being his property	5	7	0
20th July 1748 Paid Thomas Ashcroft for getting and dressing stone at Dean for Tarleton lock	4	4	8

Stretches of the river banks gave much trouble, the worst length being at Crooke, and there are very many payments for the repair of Crooke banks.

In order to get more water into the river, money was spent on diverting two streams into it near its source on Rivington Moor. Richard Melling, the well-known Wigan surveyor and engineer, carried out this work. Thomas Higginson was another surveyor employed by the navigation, and in September 1748 he was paid 10s (50p) for levelling land at Croston. In 1749, the proprietors thought of extending the navigation to Hindley by means of Borsdane Brook. John Sargeant, surveyor, and his assistants were paid £1 2s 11d (£1.14½) 'for trying of ye level from Pettycoat Lane in Ince to near ye Ffour Lane Ends in Hindley in order to have brought Baesden Brook into there if practicable — but we found a ffall of 23 feet 4 inches'.

Some local people were not in favour of the river traffic. In October 1748 Robert Caunce of Rufford was charged 'with throwing stones in ye river to stop ye passage'.

Many bricks were made for the navigation proprietors, mainly at Tarleton and at Pool Bridge and Miry Lane in Wigan:

	£	s	d
6th May 1741 Paid Jeffrey Barrow for carting soil off the Strines and coal and slack to the Brick Kiln at Miry Lane end	4	14	8

In the previous October William Tindsley was paid £5 for carting clay for bricks in the land above Pool Bridge. The price of bricks was 9s 6d (47½p) per thousand and the accounts show that large quantities were made. In December 1745 John Bibye was paid £3 for carting 120,000 bricks to Tarleton and in the following May he received £4 17s 6d (£4.87½) for moulding 30,000 bricks there. The rate for moulding was 3s 2d (16p) per thousand but for 'kilning' 60,000 bricks in that year he received only £1 10s 0d (£1.50). During the summer of 1746 110,000 bricks were made at Tarleton for the river proprietors. By 1748 the figure had risen to 140,000.

The main purchasers of limestone were Messrs Holmes and Wigan, who purchased it for sale to improvers of land. Local landowners such as William Bankes of Winstanley, Leigh Master of New Hall, Roger Holt of Ince and James Bradshaw of Newburgh purchased considerable quantities of lime. In 1745 William Bankes bought 50 tons, and the same amount in 1746, whilst Leigh Master purchased 59 tons in 1745. The price was 5s (25p) per ton at the river. In 1750 a contract was entered into with Messrs Holmes and Wigan that they should take all the limestone from the river company for seven years. However, William Bankes and others still managed to purchase their own direct from the river proprietors.

Coal Supplies To The Douglas Navigation
From Outside The Orrell Area

Of course, much of the coal carried on the Douglas Navigation came from collieries outside the Orrell Coalfield. Considerable quantities of the famous Haigh cannel were carted from Sir Roger Bradshaigh's pits to the River Douglas at Pool Bridge for sale to customers of the river proprietors and there are many entries similar to the following:

	£	s	d
28th Sept. 1741. Paid Ralph Lowe for carting cannel from Haigh to Pool Bridge for sale by the river	8	0	0
16th Nov. 1743. Paid John Pearson for carting 1,000 baskets of cannel from Haigh to ye river at 18d per score	4	10	0
9th Dec. 1743. Cannel had of Sir Roger Bradshaigh at Haigh this summer and now at ye basin, 4,000 baskets	60	0	0

Ralph Widdows and William Burrows were paid 19s (95p) for 'piling up' this cannel at the basin. John Pearson, William Glazebrook and James Welsh were constantly engaged on carting cannel to the river, and very many payments were made for 'shoveling up' cannel at the basin. Pilfering is not entirely a twentieth-century vice, John Mitton being given a shilling for, 'watching the cannel one night because we thought it was stoln'.

Perhaps a brief digression on the subject of the remarkable Wigan cannel is of interest. The late Earl of Crawford and Balcarres stated that his ancestors, the Bradshaighs, had left records of the working of the cannel mines at Haigh from the fourteenth century onwards. Cannel is hard, compact and lustrous and has been described as 'the choicest coal in England'. It was at its best under the townships of Haigh, Aspull, Ince, Standish and Wigan (the old borough) but it thinned out in adjacent townships. For example, it disappears altogether on the north-eastern boundary of Winstanley Park. It is well known that during the eighteenth and early nineteenth centuries, many figures were carved from cannel, mostly by Robert Town of Wigan, and many examples of this are in the British Museum. As a fuel it was superb, and Lord Crawford said that 'the high calorific value, the rich yield of gas, the brilliance of its flame, the steadiness of its combustion, the cleanliness of the raw fuel and its ashlessness when burned' earned it a world-wide reputation, and indeed it was being sold in Paris in 1788. Further supplies of cannel were sought at Aspull. In July 1744 a messenger was sent to William Hollinshead, the auditor at Highfield cannel pits (Aspull), to enquire about purchasing cannel there. Later in the century the Hollinshead family owned an estate with a colliery at Blackrod.

Alexander Leigh worked a colliery at Tunstead near Halfway House in Pemberton, and supplied large quantities of coal to the river. The seams worked there were the Pemberton Five Feet and Four Feet Seams, which, although of good quality, were not equal to the Orrell seams. Leigh also sent ironstone to the river, several bands of this occurring below the Pemberton Five Feet Seam:

	£	s	d
3rd August 1745 Paid John Cooper for carting 5 score and 5 baskets of coal from Tunstead pit on 13th and 14th June for the river at 16d per score		7	0

Cooper was subsequently paid 12d (5p) per score for the same job, but 16d (7p) was paid only when the road to Wigan was bad due to wet weather. James Walthew and Ralph Bradshaw carted much coal from the Tunstead pits to the river at rates varying with the state of the roads and the weather ie from 10d (4p) to 16d (7p) per score.

In March 1747 Leigh sent 121 tons 15 baskets to Poulton at a price of 3s 10d (19p) per ton. In the previous year he had despatched 52 tons to the same place as well as 77 tons of 'sleck'. This slack was probably used in the salt manufacture or for making bricks.

The Gerard family of Bryn and Garswood had worked the coal mines on their estates for many generations, and although the Douglas Navigation lay at a considerable distance from his pits, Sir Thomas Gerard took advantage of it to dispose of his coal. Besides coal, however, there were many entries concerning cannel:

	£	s	d
28th May 1747 Paid Sir Thomas Gerard's auditor John Martland for 10 tons of cannel at 21 to the score	2	7	6

In July 1749 a messenger was sent to Mr Cullen (probably the steward) at Garswood about purchasing cannel and this resulted in 60 tons 16 cwts being sent to the river at a price of 5s (25p) per ton at the pit. The cartage totalled 13s 4d (66½p).

It is difficult to see from where Sir Thomas Gerard obtained his cannel, as there is no true cannel seam in the Bryn-Garswood district or in the Windle area. His kinsfolk and namesakes at Ince however, had the Wigan cannel seam in their grounds and it was equal to that of Haigh in quality and 3in thicker at 40in. There is no doubt that the Sir Thomas mentioned in the accounts was of the Bryn-Garswood family, as the owner of the Ince estate was Richard Gerard from 1724 to 1743 when he died. He (Richard Gerard) was succeeded by William Gerard who died in the same year and the estate then went to his sisters Mary and Elizabeth. The latter never married, but Mary married John Walmesley. Their children built Westwood House at Ince and the family resided there until the 1890s. Sir Thomas Gerard of Garswood was trustee of the estate for the two sisters and was thus able to dispose of the cannel. The mineral estate at Ince was purchased from the Gerards by the Earl of Balcarres in 1808.

In August 1748 a messenger was sent by the navigation proprietors to James Stock to enquire about possible coal supplies. Stock was the lessee of a colliery in the Hawkley Estate. At the same time Molyneux, the owner of the estate, was working a colliery there himself. It is possible that Stock may have belonged to the same family as the well-known Ashton and Billinge colliery owners Samuel Stock and Aaron Stock. Aaron, incidentally, was the despised and bullying husband of Miss Weeton the diarist.

In 1770 the Hawkley colliery was advertised:

> to be let upon a lord's part to the highest bidder for a term of three years with all and every whimsey, geer, tackle and appurtenances thereto belonging and necessary for working the same, where there is a constant sale for any quantity that can be raised.

Thomas Johnson the auditor was to show prospective lessees round the works and the auction was at 'the house of Mr Bullock, being the Eagle and Child in Wigan aforesaid on Friday the sixth day of April 1770 at 5 o'clock in the evening'. Woolworth's store now occupies the site of the Eagle and Child which in more recent times was known as the Royal Hotel.

In January 1752 Joshua Tunstall, the miller at the water corn-mill at Parbold, was paid 5s (25p) to compensate him for trespass on his land by the carters of coal to the river from John Taylor & Co's coal pits at Parbold. These pits worked the Sand Rock Seam (the lowest seam of the coal measures and of poor quality) in the fields known as the Coal Pit Fields on the Parbold village side of the quarry on the hill. The Lower Mountain Seam was also worked on the north side of Parbold Hill and some of this was despatched to Ulverston. James Bradshaw had an interest in this colliery as well as his partnership in a colliery at Orrell. He owned the farm formerly known as 'King Bradshaw's Farm' but now known as Douglas Farm in Bradshaw Lane in Parbold. One wonders if he became so wealthy and important out of his coal business that local people gave him the epithet 'King'.

Other cannel pits worked at this period were those of Roger Holt on his Ince Hall Estate. His vessel *The Swan* made regular trips with cannel down the river and along the coast to various destinations north.

In the 1750s John Kendrick who owned the Kirkless Hall Estate sank several shafts to the cannel seam. His partners were Thomas Barton, John Hodson, Richard Hatton and James Winstanley. The latter two are frequently mentioned in the Navigation accounts as shippers of cannel and coal down the river.

The Douglas Navigation seemed to prosper, and there are many entries relating to tonnage paid to the undertakers in the 1760s and 1770s. Some of these payments are from old customers such as Thomas Wigan (probably the son of James Wigan who, along with his partner Holmes, had the monopoly of the limestone carriage), James Bradshaw, Samuel Bold, Roger Holt, James Winstanley and William Hodson. Alexander Leigh still owned twenty-nine out of the thirty-six shares in the navigation. Two shares had been sold to Lord Pollington and David Poole in 1753, and before 1767 Sir John Saville had also acquired a holding in the navigation, but the remainder were still held by Robert Holt's legatees. However, in 1771 Alexander Leigh sold all his shares to the newly-formed Leeds and Liverpool Canal Co. His son Holt Leigh wrote in his diary for the 16 November 1771: 'My father sold the Navigation of the River Douglas to the Leeds committee for £14,500'. He meant that his father had sold his twenty-nine shares at £500 a share. Almost immediately afterwards, Holt Leigh bought 'My uncle Holt's share of the River Douglas', and also his uncle John Chadwick's share for £300 each and on the fifth of the following February he sent £300 to Mr Roberts at Bath to pay for Mr Poole's share.

1.6 THE LEEDS AND LIVERPOOL CANAL

Some excellent accounts have been written about the history of the Leeds and Liverpool canal, notably those by A.E. Killick law clerk to the Canal Co in the 1880s and recently by Charles Hadfield in *The Canals of North West England* (see bibliography), so only a brief description of its origins is given here.

Aikin stated in 1795 that

> a navigation between the Eastern and Western seas by means of the Aire and Ribble had for many years been thought of as a practicable and useful work, and some endeavours had been used to draw attention to it but ineffectually.

According to Killick, however, the great commercial and financial success of the Duke of Bridgewater's canal was

> at once recognised as marking a distinct and most important advance in carrying facilities. One horse could draw from 40 to 50 tons weight and this resulted in the price of coal in Manchester being cut by 50%.

This statement needs to be qualified as the coal had to be transhipped into carts and this sometimes made it dearer than coal brought directly from the pits in one journey.

The Duke's canal, and the success of the Sankey Canal, Lancashire's first canal, constructed by Henry Berry, a pupil of Thomas Steers, excited business peoples' interest in canals. Hence John Longbothom, an engineer said to have been a pupil of Smeaton (who amongst many other things built the Eddystone Lighthouse) and also of James Brindley, brought out a scheme for constructing a canal between Leeds and Liverpool. John Hustler of Bradford became intensely interested in this scheme and a meeting of interested parties was advertised for the 2 July 1766 at the Sun Inn in Bradford. A committee was appointed and in 1770 an Act of Parliament was obtained authorising a capital of £260,000 with power to raise a further £60,000 if required.

John Longbothom was given the task of constructing the canal whilst John Hustler became the treasurer and from then on he directed most of his energies to the project. He was in partner-

ship with Edmund Peckover and they were the leading woolstaplers
in Bradford. It is interesting to note that Edmund Peckover, his
son Jonathan and John Hustler's eldest son William, along with
several others, were to become partners in 1779 in the 'grand
lease' of all the mines under the Standish estate in Standish, Shevington, Worthington, Coppull, Duxbury and Wigan. Also John Hustler and his sons became important colliery owners in our Orrell
belt, so it may be of interest to know what kind of a person John
Hustler was. An obituary notice about him in the *Gentleman's
Magazine* for November 1790 stated:

> To the greatness of his mind is the nation indebted for the design of
> uniting the East and West seas by means of a Canal Navigation from
> Leeds to Liverpool. For Twenty years past, unwearied was his atten-
> tion to this his darling object and by the unremitting anxiety and con-
> cern which he felt for its completion and prosperity, it is to be feared
> his days were shortened.

Another article said of him

> He was a man of great foresight, energy and tact and took a large share
> in that immense undertaking, the formation of the Leeds and Liverpool
> canal of which he was the organising genius, sparing neither time nor
> money.

He was a Quaker with all the large-heartedness and business acumen
which has so often distinguished members of the Society of Friends,
and within the Society he and his sons were powerful leaders.
By their intermarriages they became related to many of the most
wealthy and influential members of this important body of people.

The original bill for the canal was passed by both Houses of
Parliament by May 1770 after some opposition from the shareholders in the Douglas Navigation. Their opposition to the bill was
due to a proposed aqueduct carrying the canal over the Douglas
at Newburgh which would prevent the use of masts and cause
other inconveniences. This was overcome by a provision to build
connecting cuts to the canal on each side, with locks as necessary.

Holt Leigh, son of Alexander Leigh and a lawyer like his father,
who was then eighty-three years old, went to London to represent
his father during the committee stage of the Bill. The route he
took is rather unusual:

> 8th Feb 1770 Set out from Wigan for London in our postchaise about
> the Leeds canal. Lay at Leek. 9th Feb. Lay at Leicester. 10th Feb. Lay
> at Dunstable. 11th Feb. got to London about 1 o'clock and lay at the
> George in Aldermanbury. 12th Feb. lay at my lodgings at Mrs Bushell's
> in York Buildings. March 19th. Committee upon the Leeds Bill.

This continued for nine days and ended on the 4 April. After the passing of the bill there was a meeting of the Douglas commissioners at the Eagle and Child at Newburgh, no doubt to consider the effect the canal was going to have on their undertaking.

By June 1770 £172,400 had been subscribed and a committee of management twenty-two in number had been elected, which besides Hustler included Thomas Hardcastle of Bradford, who was to become his partner in the collieries in Orrell, and Jonathan Blundell of Liverpool, who founded a colliery concern in Orrell that was to extend into the adjoining township of Pemberton and become one of the most important firms in Lancashire. John Hollinshead a merchant of Liverpool but a native of Chorley and a friend of Blundell was also on the committee.

Besides the Yorkshire committee, a Lancashire committee composed of Liverpool merchants was formed, James Brindley was instructed to carry out a check survey and report on Longbothom's scheme. He pronounced it very practicable. The Liverpool committee also engaged John Ives and Richard Melling, the Wigan surveyor to survey possible alternative routes on their behalf and they recommended a considerable alteration in Longbothom's route through Lancashire. However, Whitworth, another surveyor appointed by the Yorkshire committee, stated that Ives and Melling were 49ft out in their levels and this discredited them. John Hollinshead was chairman and treasurer of the Liverpool committee. The Yorkshire committee desired the shortest route between Leeds and Liverpool, but the Lancashire committee wanted the canal to pass through the coalfields and manufacturing towns of the Lancashire side and thus pick up more trade and be of greater benefit to them. This controversy was eventually settled and further bills were passed in 1790 and 1791 which altered Longbothom's line through Lancashire but left the Yorkshire line as he originally proposed it.

On 4 November 1771 Holt Leigh met John Longbothom at Newburgh 'about setting out the aqueduct over the River Douglas'. This was three weeks before his father sold the navigation to the Leeds committee.

Jonathan Blundell and William Earle of Liverpool negotiated the purchase of the Douglas Navigation and were thanked by the committee for 'the extraordinary trouble' they had taken. The same minutes

ordered that Mr Balme and Mr Hardcastle be desired to go to Wigan on or before the 12th day of January next to meet Mr Longbothom there and view the collieries in that neighbourhood and to make the first payment to Mr Alexander Leigh of the money contracted to be paid for the Navigation of the River Douglas.

Several weeks later, Hardcastle reported that he went to Wigan and met Longbothom and paid Alexander Leigh £3,625 being the fourth part of his interest in the navigation:

> The Valleys being flooded, Mr Hardcastle could not look over the ground where the coal seams are supposed to be, but proceeded to Mr Bankes of Winstanley who informed the said Mr Hardcastle that in all the ground between Wigan and Newburgh, on both sides of the Douglas Navigation, are plenty of good coals, chiefly beds of from four to six feet thick.

The stretch of the canal that concerns us most was the first to be started:

> 7th Nov 1770 The Grand Canal from Leeds to Liverpool was begun near Halsall in Lancashire and was intended to be carried on from Newburgh to Liverpool with all expedition.

Thirty years purchase was the usual price paid for the land required for the canal, but some landowners demanded, and got, more. Lord Derby demanded 45 years purchase for the land on the outskirts of Liverpool, as this was continuously increasing in value. Meetings of the committee were held at the Wheatsheaf in Ormskirk whenever there was any dispute about the purchase of land, but generally it was left to Longbothom.

7   The Leeds and Liverpool Canal at Gathurst

Work proceeded apace at the two ends of the canal, from Skipton to Bingley and from Shipley to Leeds, at the Yorkshire end, and from Liverpool to Newburgh (Parbold) on the Lancashire side. The first completed section was that between Skipton and Bingley in April 1773, but that which concerns us most, from Liverpool to Gathurst, was not far behind.

Press reports, signed by Jonathan Blundell and William Earle on behalf of the Lancashire committee, and by John Hustler and William Blakey for the Yorkshire committee, kept the public informed as to the progress made. On the 8 October 1774 the *Leeds Intelligencer* contained the following account of the opening of the canal for the whole distance between Liverpool and Wigan but this included the Douglas Navigation from Gathurst to Wigan:

> On Wednesday last, the part of the Leeds canal between Liverpool and Wigan was opened with great festivity and rejoicings. The water had been let into the basin the evening before. At nine, the proprietors sailed up the canal on their barge, preceded by another filled with music with flying colours etc. and returned about one. They were saluted by two Royal Salutes of twenty-one guns each, besides the swivels on board the boats and welcomed with the repeated shouts of the numerous crowds assembled on the banks who made a most cheerful and agreeable sight. The gentlemen then adjourned to a tent where a cold collation was provided for them and their friends. From thence they went in procession to Georges Coffee House where an elegant dinner was provided. The workmen 215 in number walked first with their tools on their shoulders and cockades in their hats and were afterwards plentifully regaled of a dinner provided for them. The bells rang all day and the greatest joy and order prevailed on the occasion.

A few months previously, Jonathan Blundell, William Earle, John Hustler and William Blakey had made an inspection of the canal and concluded their report as follows

> In the course of our journey, we made particular enquiry about the business likely to come upon the canal and had the pleasure to find that there would be a great demand for the Douglas coals at Liverpool and upon the line, that very large stacks of that article are now ready upon the banks of the Navigation and at the collieries, and that the business in this part is likely to set very extensively.

Coal yards were set up at the basin at Liverpool by merchants intent on either opening collieries at Orrell or in the surrounding townships adjoining the canal, or in simply purchasing coal and transporting it along the canal to Liverpool for sale there. One example of this was the partnership of Jonathan Blundell, William Earle, Samuel Warren and Edward Chaffers. Jonathan Blundell's name was to become famous in the Wigan coalfields as his descendants owned the Pemberton Collieries until 1929 and the

8 Dean Locks on the Leeds and Liverpool Canal. The remains of the lock into the Douglas Navigation can be seen between the Lock House and the tree on the river bank

9 Dean Locks. The Leeds and Liverpool Canal was completed from Liverpool to here in 1774

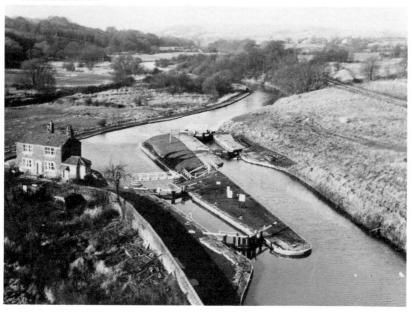

minerals there until they were nationalised in 1942. Most of the coal depots in Liverpool now owned by Cory Brothers, the big coal factors, were owned by Blundells until 1929.

It had been felt necessary to replace the old Douglas Navigation and initially an extension of the canal had been made from Newburgh to Dean, incorporating a cut begun by Alexander Leigh. At Dean a lock was made into the Douglas. In April 1776 the section from Dean to Wigan was authorised and carried out shortly afterwards. A branch canal from Burscough to Tarleton replaced the Lower Douglas Navigation and this was opened in October 1781.

To conclude, the whole of the subscribed capital had been expended by 1777 when 58 miles, or more than half of the canal had been completed. Wrangles over the route caused further delays and it was not until 1816 that the final completion of the canal from Liverpool to Leeds was accomplished. This canal, or at least the Wigan to Liverpool section, was for three-quarters of a century by far the principal means of transport for the coal produced in the Orrell coalfield. Although this means of transporting the local coals was gradually superseded by the Lancashire and Yorkshire Railway Co in the latter years of the nineteenth century, the Leeds and Liverpool Canal continued to serve the purpose for which it was originally constructed until well into the first half of the twentieth century.

CHAPTER TWO

Technical Developments

2.1 THE SEARCH FOR COAL

At the beginning of the period under review, very little was known about the geological structure of the Orrell coalfield and many boreholes were put down in Orrell · and the surrounding townships in order to prove coal, especially where it was faulted. For instance, John Halliwell and John Heskin having leased the Orrell Hall Colliery in 1756, were, by 1760, in dispute with their lessors, the heirs of Samuel Prescott, alleging that the mines were almost exhausted. The 40yd Grand Dyke Fault trends N80°W through the estate — cutting across Springs Road, 70yds south of Orrell Hall Barn. Although the easily-got Five Feet Coal on the upthrow side of the fault had been extensively worked, the coal on the downthrow side was still unproved. Halliwell put 130 boreholes down to prove the coal thoroughly and also to supply the evidence he required in the law suit with his lessors. It must have been a shock to him, to discover that the coal on the south or downthrow side was so much deeper than the coal already being worked at the colliery, and he complained that 'the coal that remains lies about 52 yards deeper. Auger Hole deep to the bottom of the coal 64 yards 1 foot 4 inches and 3 inches in hard stone and all the coal at the above depth'.

The valuation of some of the estates surrounding Orrell Hall in the middle of the eighteenth century shows how important it was to prove coal in an estate. This valuation states that no mines (seams) of coal were known or proved in Catterall's estate at Kitt Green, Thomas Atherton's estate and Thomas Ward's estate near Orrell Post. The first was only worth £1 per Cheshire acre, the second £2 per acre and the third, where apparently there was some slight prospect of coal, £3 15s (£3.75) per acre. In contrast one seam proved under John Atherton's land raised the value up to £80 an acre and similarly Naylor's (between Orrell Post and Spencer's Lane on the north side of Orrell Road) was valued at £70 an acre. In 1825 30 statute acres of land in Orrell containing three seams with a total thickness of 9ft was sold for £24,000.

There were many disappointments and half a century after Halliwell's law suit another Orrell firm, Messrs Woodcock and Haliburton, were running into trouble. Thomas Woodcock was a Wigan solicitor and his partner Alexander Haliburton had come to Wigan from Inverkeithing, originally to manage the Haigh Collieries and Ironworks for the Earl of Balcarres. They had taken out a lease of coal under the Rev J. Barton's Norley estate and also under part of the Duke of Bridgewater's estate in the Lamberhead Green area. Unfortunately, only a very small portion of Barton's estate lay in the Orrell coal belt as the Great Pemberton Fault and its accompanying 'smash' zone ran near the boundary of it. In September 1809 Woodcock agreed to 'make another trial though rendered almost hopeless by the attempts that have failed'. Hopes were raised only to be dashed, and after writing in May 1811 that 'prospects from borings very fair, Five Feet coal found in first hole at 55 yards 2ft 6ins'. Woodcock goes on to say 'a riding coal or certain indications of the other was found in the second hole at about 36 yards although it is feared there is some fault between them. Now trying third hole'.

The final letter from Woodcock on this matter some thirteen years later stated that 'with great exertion and at immense expense, we have endeavoured to prove Mr Barton's coal but have not yet succeeded'. In the meantime they had paid the Rev J. Barton £1,200 in certain rent and were pressing for reimbursement of this money. The site of the boring was in the Carr Lane — Norley Cricket field area.

The tools used in boring during that period comprised the following: *Bore rods* 1in square and 6ft or 9ft long with lengtheners 6in to 30in long. These had male and female screw joints at each end. They were made of wrought iron. *Steel chisels* 18in long with a 2in or 2½in cutting edge. *The wimble* 3ft long, hollow and cylindrical with an opening in the side, was used for bringing up borings and for boring in soft clay. *The sludger,* similar to the above without the opening, but fitted with a clack at the bottom for retaining and bringing up borings. *The beche* was used for recovering broken rods. It was hollow and slightly bell shaped, 2ft in length. *The brace head* consisted of 2 pieces of ash 3in in diameter tapering towards the end, and fixed through 2 eyes set at right angles formed in a piece of iron which screwed onto the top rod.

The method of boring was to erect first a headgear or 'three legs' consisting of 3 larch poles, approximately 12ft long and 4 to 6in diameter and fixed as a triangle. A small pulley was slung from the large bolt fastening the three legs at the top. A rope was passed over the pulley, one end of which was attached to a 'crab' or hand winch which was fitted with a pawl and brake. This was used for removing and replacing the rods in the hole. Four men, one at each end of the bracehead, lifted and turned the rods and

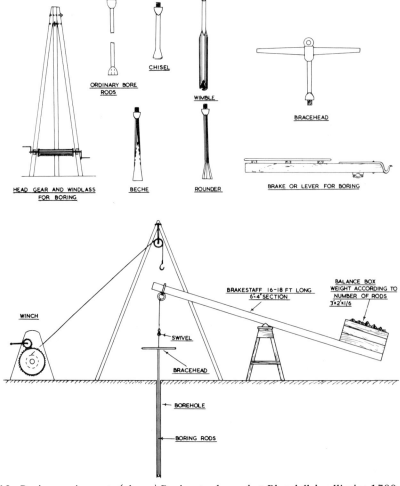

10 Boring equipment. *(above)* Boring tools used at Blundells' collieries 1780-
    1940 *(below)* Hand percussive method using a balance box at Pemberton
    Collieries

by this means a depth of 80ft could be reached. For greater depths
a brake-staff was used. This was a wooden lever approximately
16ft in length and 6in by 6in in section. The fulcrum was 18in
to 2ft from the end, where an iron strap hook was bolted onto it.
Sometimes a spring pole was used for deep holes instead of a brake-
staff. This method is said to have been used by the Chinese 3,000

years ago; they used bamboo for the spring pole, but in Lancashire larch poles generally about 20ft long were used (Fig 10).

The boring operation was performed simply by raising the rods, turning them slightly and allowing them to fall by their own weight, so that the chisel bored a circular hole and did not fasten itself. At intervals the wimble or sludger was substituted for the chisel and, by means of the clack valve at the base, the cuttings and sludge at the bottom of the hole were worked into the barrel of the sludger by reciprocating it in the hole. The sludger was then brought up and its contents were examined, this being the only evidence of the strata penetrated. Gripping or retaining keys were used to prevent the rods falling back into the hole when unscrewing them. Borers were paid on contract, the rate increasing with the depth. Halliwell speaks of 1s (5p) per yard for boring as a 'Common and fear price'. At one time three of his men bored to the coal and through it 7in before they knew of the coal, 'but the real reason was they loved easey work and thought that mettle too hard'.

Generally a master borer and four men were employed. A short extract from a mid-nineteenth century boring journal below, shows the speed at which boring was accomplished to a depth of 60yd both in strong sandstone and in softer coal measure strata:

Nov 13th to 27th	Strong white rock 6 yards
Nov 27th to Dec 11th	Strong white rock 5 yards 1 ft 6 ins.
Dec 11th to Dec 14th	Sharp strong metal 1 yard 2 feet. Strong dark grey linsey 3 yards and 1 foot. Blue metal with iron bands 6 yards. Dark metal 1 yard 1 ft 6 ins. Black bass 1 yard 1 foot. Warrant and bass 1 foot. Black bass 1 ft 2 ins.

Progress at that depth was thus approximately 3yd a week in hard sandstone and 7yd a week in sandy shales, black bass and fireclay.

Attached to this boring journal are some accounts for the purchase and repair of tools. Steel was brought from Sheffield and was welded by the blacksmith to the wrought-iron drill tool to form the lower portion of it and the actual cutting edge.

	s	d
Carriage of steel from Sheffield		10
Steel for chisels	10	9
New drill 28lb at 3d	7	0
Piecing and sharping drill	2	0

(Carpenters' and other tools were made in this way up to the beginning of the present century). The auger head weighed 39lb and

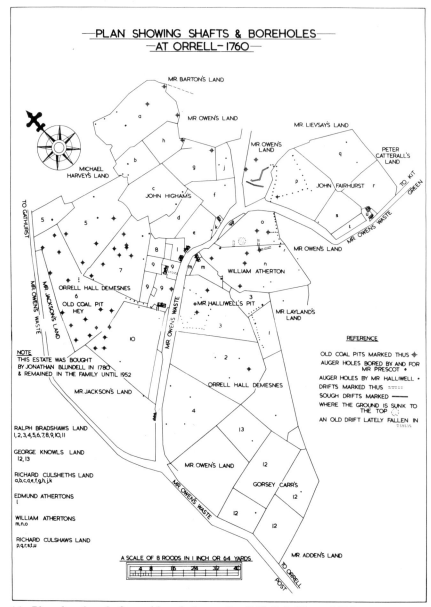

11   Plan showing shafts and boreholes at Orrell Hall Colliery, 1760

at 2½d per lb cost 8s 1d (40½p). The chisel bits had to be sharpened at very frequent intervals and spare ones were always kept in readiness for changing as and when necessary. This depended on the hardness of the strata being penetrated. The spring pole appears to have been felled in the local woods.

The snatch block which hung from the three legs, the keys for unscrewing the rods, the 'slutch [sludger] pump' and the crab (or winch) are also mentioned in the accounts, along with the 'cat foot' which was a pulley on a bracket at ground level.

2.2 PIT SHAFTS

A great many pit shafts were sunk in the Orrell area, due mainly to the shallow depths of the two seams. For example forty-seven pit shafts had been sunk on the rise side of the Grand Dyke Fault in the Orrell Hall estate before 1756 (Fig 11). These worked the Five Feet Coal in the area which was only 6yd 1ft 10in deep in the Barn Meadow, 11yd 0ft 11in in the Stone Delph Hey, 13yd 0ft 3in in the Rigby Meadow and 14yd 2ft 9in in the Hall Meadow. Halliwell himself sank fifteen shafts mostly on the dip side of the Grand Dyke Fault. Not far away the Rev Thomas Holme sank four new shafts in his estate in Orrell between 1774 and 1780, and in the accounts of the Winstanley Collieries of the period shaft sinking is mentioned quite frequently. Thirty-one shafts of all descriptions are shown on a 1760 plan of the Pingot area on the Winstanley-Pemberton boundary. There is no doubt that John Jackson's Salterford estate would be worked with a similar large number of shafts to the Orrell Hall estate as the Five Feet Seam under Jackson's land was very shallow. John Clarke & Co sank forty-two shafts between 1792 and 1842 to work the Orrell Four Feet Seam under 178 Cheshire acres in Winstanley. These varied from 82 to 20yd deep. Jonathan Blundell and Son had sunk at least fifty-nine shafts in Orrell between 1780 and 1810. No records are available of the number of shafts put down by the other main colliery owners in Orrell, such as Hustler and Co, Lofthouse Jarratt and Co, Woodcock and Haliburton, and Thomas Claughton, but it must have been very considerable. It is possible that no less than 350 shafts were sunk in this belt (Fig 12).

In the period under consideration the method of sinking a shaft was first to mark out its position and diameter (or dimensions if it was oval or rectangular). The thirty-one shafts mentioned above on the 1760 plan are all shown as square ones. The dimensions at the top were generally 2ft or more than the finished size, to allow for brickwork or other permanent lining.

If the ground consisted of soft earth, loam or clay, the shaft was sunk for about 6ft with pick and shovel and the earth thrown to the surface. The shaft bottom was then levelled and a cribbing ring fixed. In the case of circular shafts these consisted of segments of oak 4ft 6in long and 6in x 4in in section cut to suit the diameter of the shaft and pegged together with oak pegs about 1½in diameter. Most of the shafts in the early part of our period were 6 or 7ft in diameter, but by the early nineteenth century 8 to 9ft had become common.

After fixing the first cribbing ring on the bottom of the shaft a second one was put together, raised up about 3ft and supported on wooden props called punch props set upon the bottom ring. A third ring was fixed 3ft above the last and level with the surface, and then sometimes a fourth one to project 3ft above the surface so that the dirt from the shaft could be tipped there to start forming the pit bank. Backing deals of oak, 9ft long and 6in wide and about 1½in thick, were placed behind the cribbing all around the shaft and wedged tight. Stringing deals were then nailed on the front or inside of the rings at intervals in order to fasten the whole structure together. By this time it was necessary to fix a head-frame with a pulley and a crab or winch complete with rope and shackle, in order to wind the debris out of the shaft with a large bucket known as a 'hoppet'. Sinking was proceeded with in this way until the 'rock head' was reached. A level was then prepared on the hard stone and a walling crib approximately 12in wide and 6in thick was laid on it. This was tightly wedged against the shaft sides after making sure that its centre coincided with the centre of the shaft. The wooden lining was then removed, if possible, and the permanent shaft wall built up to the surface on the walling ring. Generally the brickwork was 9in thick but occasional examples have been found in the district that were only 4½in thick, such as the shaft discovered recently at the bottom of Gathurst Brow by the new Hoscar Sewer tunnel.

At that period in the Wigan coalfield it was the practice to leave shafts unlined where the strata was fairly hard and consequently most shafts were only lined near the surface. In 1772 Holt Leigh supplied John Longbothom with 7,150 bricks for lining three shafts at Ayrefield Colliery. Taking a figure of forty-five bricks to a square yard of 4½in brickwork this is equal to 159 square yards of lining. In a shaft 7ft diameter, 7·3 square yards of lining would be required for every yard in depth. Therefore the total depth of 4½in lining for each of the three shafts is just over 7yd. If the brickwork was 9in thick this figure would be halved. In May 1777

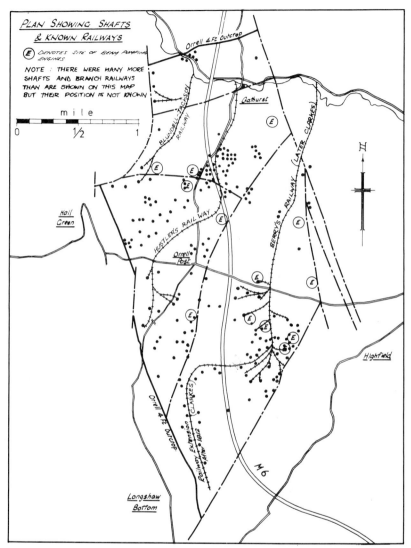

Orrell 4ft Outcrop

Gathurst

BLUNDELL-JACKSON RAILWAY

BERRY'S RAILWAY (LATER CLARKES)

Hall Green

HUSTLERS RAILWAY

Orrell Post

Highfield

Orrell 4 ft Outcrop

Railway Extension (CLARKES) after 1812

M 6

Longshaw Bottom

12   Plan showing some of the shafts and railways in the Orrell Coalfield

Hustler used 6,300 bricks for 'bricking a coalpit' and this would line a shaft 7ft diameter with 4½in brickwork for 19yds or for 9½yds with 9in brickwork.

The minimum amount of capital was expended on the pit shafts in Orrell at that time as they were shallow and had such a very short life. Rarely did a coal drawing shaft last more than three

years in the early part of the period. For example Halliwell's Great
Carr Pit had a life of 136 weeks, the Know Shift Pit 35 weeks, the
Park Pit 170 weeks and Berry's Pit 154 weeks. Engine, or pumping pits were the exception and a much better job was made of
these as generally they had to last for the life of the colliery or
the term of the lease or longer, and they housed the very expensive pumps and associated pitwork. Some of these engine shafts
were rectangular in section and lined with brickwork at the top
as was the case with Blundell & Co's Chain Colliery Engine Pit
and a recently discovered one near Prescot. Others were sometimes lined with strong timberwork.

After the brickwork had been built up from the walling ring,
sinking was continued by heavy sinking picks and hammers and
wedges if it was possible, but where sandstone or other hard and
compact strata was encountered, drilling and blasting with gunpowder was resorted to.

Some idea of the tools in use at that time is given in a bill dated
1769 for blacksmith's work supplied by Holt Leigh to John Halliwell. 'To a bolt for ye three legs 3½lb at 4d per lb'. This was the
large bolt that fastened the three posts of the head frame together
which were set up in the form of a triangle. From this strong bolt
a pulley was slung by means of a short chain and shackle. A rope
from a winch, fixed at the surface near the head frame, passed over
this pulley, a hook being secured at the end of it by bending the
rope back on itself and clamping it. 'Ironwork for a new winch
13½lb at 4d. 4s 6d.' 'to two stops for a turn 2½lb at 4d. 10d'.
A turn was a simple form of winch with the handles fixed directly
on the roll or drum, ie, it was not geared. The hoppet for winding
the broken material out of the shaft was of wood but strengthened
with iron straps and bands. A bucket was used for winding water
and a 'scoop' for lading water into it: 'To ears and plates for a
bucket 1s 4d'. 'To a scoop ironing 1s 2d'. The heavy sinking picks
were 8½lb in weight. A sinking hammer for breaking lumps of
rock was of similar weight and a drilling hammer weighed 7lb: 'To
two new sinking picks 17lb at 4d'. 'To a drilling hammer 7lb at
4½d'. Where the strata was soft or had well-defined jointing, progress was made by using the sinking pick and the sinking hammer
and wedge. The sinking wedges were small, unlike coal wedges,
and were generally about 6in long, 1½in broad and 1in thick. Those
used by Halliwell weighed just over 2lb.

When blasting with gunpowder had to be carried out, the shot
holes were generally drilled by three men by means of drilling
hammers and a set of drills. The drilling hammer had a shaft about
30in long and a head 6in long. The drilling set consisted of a short

drill approximately 18in long, a middle drill about 27in and a long drill round about 42in long. To drill a hole, one of the men held a drill in his hand and blows were dealt on the striking face by hammers swung by the other two men. After each blow the drill was drawn upwards an inch or two and turned slightly so as to form a circular hole and a scraper was used at frequent intervals to clean the drill-dust or sludge from the hole.

In softer 'mettle' a drill called a 'jumper' was sometimes used. This did not require the force of a hammer and was generally from 4ft to 6ft in length with a chisel edge at each end. The middle of the rod was bulged-out to form a heavy ball thus giving the drill greater weight. To use it a short hole was first made with a pick and then the drill was inserted and at each stroke it was jumped or pushed sharply into the hole and in this way the hole was drilled.

Before charging the hole with gunpowder, it was first cleaned by a scraper. This scraper consisted of a copper rod 4-5ft long and ¼in diameter. The end of it was flattened into a circular form of less diameter than the hole and turned up at right angles to the rod. The gunpowder charge was either loose or encased in a cartridge, but before putting it into the hole, a copper pricker which was a rod of copper of small diameter terminating in a point, was inserted into it and by this means the charge was pushed to the bottom of the hole. The pricker was left sticking in the charge during the tamping or stemming of the hole. The tamping or stemming rod for forcing the clay stemming into the hole was usually made of copper about 3-4ft long and of semicircular form with a small groove along it for the pricker.

When the tamping was completed the pricker was slowly and carefully withdrawn leaving a narrow hole through the tamping to the charge. A straw containing a train of powder was then inserted into the hole with a piece of touch paper attached at the outer end. The longest and best straws for this purpose were picked from the corn fields before harvesting began. The touch paper was lit and when it burnt the straw it ignited the powder, which in its turn fired the charge. It can be well imagined that wet strata would cause much trouble with misfired shots and a lot of skill and patience would be required in stemming and firing the holes. The pattern of drilling was first to blast a wedge out of the middle of the shaft and afterwards to 'flank off' to this until the required diameter was achieved.

Sinking rates for the shallow coal-drawing shafts of the Orrell belt in the mid-eighteenth century varied between 7s (35p) and 13s (65p) per yard. In the 1760s William Bankes of Winstanley paid 8s (40p) per yard for sinking and provided the powder 'if it be necessary'. John Halliwell paid a sliding scale increasing with depth of 10s (50p), 15s (75p) and one guinea (£1.05) per yard for the sinking of a shaft 57yd deep. For sinking an engine pit he paid £1 per yard from the top to 22½yd down, £1 10s (£1.50) per yard for the next 27½yd and £1 15s (£1.75) for the remaining 8yd at the bottom.

An early example of the use of wooden tubbing to sink through running sand was recently discovered when the Skelmersdale link with the M6 motorway was constructed. It was one of Blundells' shafts at the Edge Hall Colliery which had been sunk through several yards of running sand near the surface. The lining was formed by a wooden cylinder of oak cribbing rings 3ft apart backed by boards 6in wide by 1.1/8in thick nailed to them on the outside. At the bottom end of the cylinder a cutting shoe was attached and brickwork was built up on the rings inside the backing deals to provide sufficient weight for the cylinder to sink through the sand to the hard rock head. When this was reached, the wet sand and mud would be excavated from the inside of the cylinder or tubbing, and sinking would then proceed in the normal way.

An example of the time taken in sinking a shaft was the Park Pit at the Orrell Fire Engine Colliery sunk in the Park Field immediately east of the Old Engine public house. It was 42yd deep to the Orrell Five Foot Seam and it took two sinkers 24 weeks to complete it, from October 1771 to 21 March 1772 an average progress of 1¼yd per week. On 23 April 1774 the Great Carr Pit reached the Orrell Five Feet Seam at a depth of 47yds. It had taken four men 17 weeks to sink it, an average progress of just over 2¼yd per week. Good progress was made in shallow shafts, William Bankes's men completing a 17½yd shaft in three weeks in 1766.

On the other hand, where excessive water was encountered and where a large proportion of the strata consisted of hard sandstone, sinking was a very slow and difficult process. Thus Blundells' Bye Pit at Pemberton, commenced in the second decade of the nineteenth century, took 179 weeks and 3 days to sink 130yd. It was 9ft 6in in diameter and unlined except near the surface.

The practice of sinking large numbers of shafts to work comparatively small areas of coal persisted well into the nineteenth century in this district; a diary kept by one of Blundells' officials shows that the firm sank eleven shafts between 13 April 1812 and 6 February 1819.

One of the chief reasons for the sinking of so many shafts was the primitive transport arrangements underground. Until the 1830s the system of drawing baskets on sledges to the pit shafts was common. The colliers were paid so much for a score of baskets 'hung upon the hook', in other words their rate included drawing to the shaft bottom or pit 'eye'. 'Long drawing' rates had to be paid for drawing over a certain distance. In 1730 at Harrock Hill Colliery three miles from Orrell, long drawing commenced at 40yd from the pit eye and the following increases in payment were made:

Between						
	40	—	56	yd	..	½d per score
	56	—	72	yd	..	1d per score
	72	—	80	yd	..	1½d per score
	80	—	120	yd	..	2d per score
	120	—	136	yd	..	2½d per score
	232	—	248	yd	..	6d per score

2.3 THE WORKING OF THE COAL

In the working of the shallow Orrell Five Feet Seam it was usual to get only a certain percentage of the seam leaving many small pillars of coal in the seam unworked. All the leases in the early part of our period stipulated that the lessees must: 'leave substantial and firm pillars of coal at proper due distances sufficient to support the roof of the hollows to prevent the upper grounds from falling in'.

Many shafts were sunk from 30 to 100yd apart. Some of these old workings have been reopened from time to time by optimists who thought the pillars might be worth working. In 1928 the old Orrell Five Feet works were opened up on the Dean House estate and the pillars were found to be 3yd square on average, the roadways being 5ft wide. These had previously been opened out on another part of the same estate in 1874 when it was found that the pillars were 2-3yd square and the roads 1½yd wide. Under Bankes's estate (Holmes) on the eastern side of Dean Wood, pillars up to 4yd square were recorded. In the other part of the old Holmes estate near Holland House, in the Orrell Four Feet Seam, the roads were again found to be 1½yd wide and the pillars 3yd wide in 1934, but no length is recorded.

At Blundell's Orrell House estate the following measurements were recorded when a narrow road was driven through the old pillars: road 1½yds, pillar 2yds, road 1½yds, pillar 1½yds, road 1½yds, pillar 11yds, road 1½yds, pillar 2yds, road 1½yds, pillar 7yds, road 1½yds, pillar 8yds.

In setting out the roadways in those days the two main consid-
erations were the dip or inclination of the seam and the direction
of the cleavage or main cleat, the latter being the more important.
In the case of the Orrell seams as in most British coals, except
anthracite and cannel, there are two distinct planes nearly vertical
crossing the laminations (which are parallel to the bedding plane)
and it is easy to split a piece of coal along these planes. The main
cleat is much more well-defined than the secondary cleat which
is sometimes stepped. 'Endways' or 'ends' were driven parallel to
the main cleat and generally speaking were more difficult to drive
than roads driven on the 'face' at right angles to the main cleat.
A higher yardage rate was always paid for driving a road 'on end'
than for driving one on the 'face'. In Lancashire they had their
own version of the 'pillar and stall' method of working. It is still
referred to as 'straitwork' (or was until a generation ago) and the
roads as 'strait places'. This is an excellent description of the many
miles of roads 1½yd wide driven in the two seams at Orrell. Over
a hundred years ago John Warburton a Lancashire colliery manager noted:

> I have known men constitutionally old and finished at 34 years of age
> in consequence of working in straitwork. Besides the extra labour in
> this class of work there is a certain amount of oppresiveness owing to
> the small and confined space in which the work is performed. So con-
> fined is it that the men not only breathe again the same air, but inhale
> a great amount of coal dust, so much so that their discharges are as
> black as coal itself. There is a good deal of hard labour in straitwork.

The writer remembers many strait places being driven by hand
at Blundells' Pemberton Colliery as late as the 1930s but at that
time they were more than twice the width of those of the eighteenth and early nineteenth centuries at their Orrell collieries.

The method of driving these straits was first to undercut or
'hole' the seam, generally at the bottom, although near the middle
of the Orrell Five Feet Seam there was a dirt band which was sometimes cut out for the holing. This holing was done to a depth of
2ft 6in to 3ft 6in and from side to side. In some of the old narrow
roads I have seen in the district it is obvious that 'nicking' or side
cutting was resorted to as well as holing. This means that they cut
grooves at the face of the road down each side from roof to floor,
with a pick. Doing this in addition to holing increased very considerably the work of the collier as he had so much more cutting to
do. This was the miner's most laborious work in those days, the
men who did it being considered the cream of the miners. All
this holing and cutting however caused a considerable waste of the
seam as it produced much slack which was mostly unsaleable.

Holing picks had straight blades 18in long from tip to tip and about 2lb in weight. The shaft was at least 3ft long and sometimes as much as 4ft. A curious custom referred to as 'helving the hack' or 'hauming the hack' allowed each collier a score of coals every New Year, each drawer half a score of coals and the winders, browmen, smith and auditor 1 score each. The writer remembers a pick shaft referred to as a pick 'haum'.

After the holing and side cutting was finished sometimes it would be possible to get the coal down in large pieces with a pick, but in other cases it would have to be got down by wedging or blasting. Coal wedges were about 12in long, 2½in wide by 1in thick in the middle, tapering 6in to the edge. They were also tapered the other way to the octagonal striking face. The wedge and feathers and other patent multiple wedges came into use during the nineteenth century. In November 1887 Joseph Dickinson HM Inspector of Mines noted: 'the pick, hammer and wedge remain as of old, with improvement in the wedges'.

We know that gunpowder was in common use for shaft sinking at Orrell in the eighteenth century and it is possible that it became the practice to use it in the getting of coal although this was not encouraged as it shattered the coal and made it less marketable. Fifty years ago, however, a shothole charged with gunpowder and with the straw containing the train of powder intact was discovered in Holmes's old Five Feet workings near Dean Wood. Certainly gunpowder was in common use at Orrell during the early part of the nineteenth century as John Ashurst, underlooker at Blundells' Edge Hall or Slycroft Colliery, stated that after a 'creep' in the Four Feet Seam when the floor had lifted it became so solid 'that we have had to blow it the same as rock'.

Creeps seem to have been more frequent in the Four Feet Seam than in the Five Feet, probably because of the greater depth and because the 'warrant' or fireclay floor was softer. A creep occurred when the pillars were too small, the weight forcing them down into the soft floor, and causing it to rise in the roads. Once a creep set in, it spread slowly but surely over the whole of the workings. No amount of timbering would retard its progress and the roadways became choked, often causing that part of the pit to be abandoned.

Halliwell had set his Aspull cannel pits out at 400yd apart on the level or strike line and 240yd between them on the full dip. He said the cannel was drawn 96yd from the dip side and 144yd from the rise side to each shaft. His shafts at Orrell were much nearer together than the Aspull ones and were less than 180yd apart in most cases. Blundells' were between 100 and 200yd apart and Clarke's from 150 to 300yd apart.

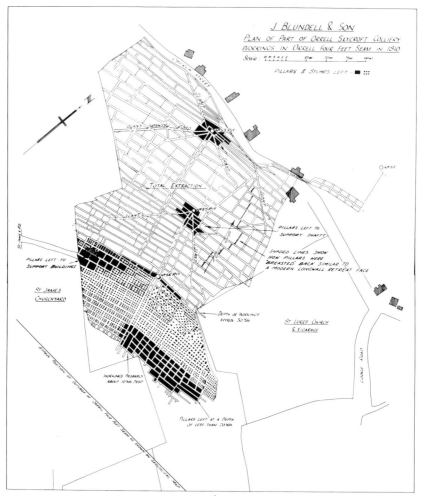

13 Plan of Blundells' Orrell Slycroft Colliery 1810

Much slack was left in the Five Feet workings but not so much
in the Four Feet as this was readily convertible into good saleable
coke.

Before the end of the eighteenth century at the large collieries
of Blundell, Hustler and Clarke a new and more rational system
of working was developed. Shafts were sunk from 150 to 200yd

apart on the level or strike line of the seam and generally the same distance apart on the dip.

Ideally, but this would not always be done because of faulting, pairs of roads were driven both on the end of the cleat and on the face between the various shafts as the colliery was gradually worked from the dip side of the leasehold up to the rise. This more or less cut the area up into panels between the shafts. The purpose of these pairs of roads was to act as drawing, drainage and ventilation roads. They were 'not less than 4 feet or more than five feet wide' and the pillars between were approximately 3yd wide and any length from 6 to 30yd.

From the roads driven on the end or 'endgates' as they were called, extraction roads were driven at right angles to the endgates and on the face of the coal forming pillars, generally 7 to 10yd wide and 70 to 90yd long. When the panel had been developed in this fashion the pillars were brought back by 'breasting', ie a stepped retreating longwall face as shown in Fig 13. There is no doubt that this new system of working would increase considerably the output per collier.

Very little timber was required in the narrow roads and it would normally only be used in bringing back the pillars. That it was used very sparingly is evident from the following extract from a letter written to Lt Col H.B.H. Blundell by his colliery agent and manager W.J. Greener on 11 September 1880 in regard to the new regulations about the support of the workings:

> also that the miner must secure the roof and sides of his own working place but it is nowhere stated where the timber is to be provided and who is to take it into the working place, *though it has been the system from all time for the collier to do so.* I know of collieries at the present day where the colliers go to the saw mill on the surface and cut their own timber, it   being held that so long as it is brought within range of the Pit there is no violation of the rule.

It can well be imagined that if the foregoing was the case in 1880 in the district, during the period when there were no rules little timber for underground supports would be provided by the colliery owners, although Bankes's UpHolland Colliery accounts show payments made to colliers for 'taking' or withdrawing props.

At Halliwell's Orrell Hall Colliery in 1771 there were eight colliers, seven drawers and two sinkers. Later on two more sinkers were taken on, but apparently from April 1774 when they finished sinking they worked as colliers until the next pit was ready for sinking. The amount of coal produced by a collier in a shift depended to some extent on the man, as always, but at Dean Colliery in the Orrell Five Feet Seam in 1775 the best men were producing

65 baskets containing 140lb of coal or 4.05 tons. The worst results were from those who produced only 1 score of 26 baskets or 1·62 tons. The low figure may have resulted from men opening out new places or working in bad places. The results for four colliers at Dean Colliery between March 17th and May 12th 1775 were as follows:

James Brown
    On 9 days he produced 1.62 tons per day
    On 9 days he produced 2.43 tons per day
    On 16 days he produced 3.24 tons per day
    On 7 days he produced 4.05 tons per day

James Fenton
    On 2 days he produced 1.62 tons per day
    On 19 days he produced 3.24 tons per day
    On 5 days he produced 4.05 tons per day
    On 1 day he produced 4.86 tons

Benjamin Parr
    On 1 day he produced 0.81 tons
    On 5 days he produced 1.62 tons per day
    On 1 day he produced 2.43 tons
    On 17 days he produced 3.24 tons per day
    On 7 days he produced 4.05 tons per day

George Turner
    On 9 days he produced 1.62 tons per day
    On 16 days he produced 2.43 tons per day
    On 7 days he produced 3.24 tons per day
    On 5 days he produced 4.05 tons per day

The Winstanley Colliery accounts show that from February 1766, when the system of paying the colliers by the load was superseded by payment by the score of baskets, regular output was maintained by all the colliers of 2 score per man per day to start with, dropping to 1½ score per man per day during the following months. The baskets contained 150lb and these were 24 to the score so that 2 score = 3.2 tons and 1½ score 2.7 tons.

A sample of the fortnightly colliers' scores at Meyrick Bankes's UpHolland colliery in 1819 shows output per man varying from 14 to 32 scores, the average being 23 scores, equal to nearly 2 scores per day (3.1 tons).

The coal was filled into baskets, which in the last half of the eighteenth century varied between 120 and 150lb capacity. For example, at Orrell Hall Colliery they were originally of 122lb capacity and at the Dean Colliery they held 140lb. They were placed on 'sleds' fitted with iron runners and were dragged by the drawers (often young boys or girls) by means of a belt or chain harness to the pit 'eye' or pit bottom where they were hooked on to the winding rope and sent up the pit. In the early part of the period the boys and girls or women employed as drawers were often related to the collier and even up to quite modern times he always appointed and paid his drawer. Sledges are frequently mentioned in Halliwell's Orrell Fire Engine Colliery accounts for the 1770s. The 1½cwt baskets used at the Hulton Pits near Bolton were 31in by 21¾in and 8in deep. Similar baskets have been found in eighteenth century workings in the Ince Yard Seam near the Ben Jonson Inn at Pemberton. A human 'guss' harness was discovered in old workings at Atherton a few years ago and placed in the Wigan Mining College.

The baskets used were made and repaired at the colliery. In 1790 £18 0s 2d was paid to Henry Blundell for a chestnut horse and basket rods supplied to Orrell Collieries. These basket rods were put in a cylinder, into which steam was blown to make them pliable for bending to the shape of the basket.

Sometimes wooden rails were used on which the sleds were drawn, and some of these were found forty years ago in the Orrell Five Feet workings near Dean Wood. They were about 5ft long, 5in wide and 1in thick. Along one edge a strip of wood 1in square was nailed. Presumably this was to prevent the sled runners coming off. In 1828 a carpenter charged £2 8s 0d for supplying '96 yards Tram Rales at 6d per yard'. Baskets were gradually increased in size and eventually trams or 'rolleys' with disc wheels, running on angle iron rails, were introduced. Empty baskets were placed on these at the pit bottom from whence they were taken to the face by the drawers, loaded there and drawn back again to the shaft, where they were hooked on to the winding rope. This was the system in use at Blundells' collieries in 1841, as reported by a Government Commissioner.

Rails were gradually improved and after 4ft and 6ft bridge rails had been introduced it was possible to use trams with flanged wheels. This soon led to the introduction of tubs, but by that time the great collieries of Orrell were coming to an end and it is most unlikely that tubs were ever introduced in them. A plan of the Four Feet Seam in Blundells' Edgehall Colliery dated 1810 shows slant roads or cross cuts radiating from some of the shafts and it is possible they were horse-roads where a horse could pull several trams laden with baskets (Fig 13).

Between 1760 and 1800 a great development had taken place in the method of working coal in Orrell. In 1760, and for some time later, it was common for only four colliers to work in one pit which lasted about two years before it was exhausted. When it finished the colliers salvaged any material there was and transferred it to the new pit ready sunk for them. This was known as 'shifting'.

Allowances were made at the new pit for opening out the 'eye' or seam inset in the shaft, and once it was opened out it carried on in the same way with the same four colliers and their drawers until in its turn it became exhausted and they 'shifted' to yet another new shaft.

Up to the last few years of the eighteenth century it was common for forty per cent of the coal to be lost in pillars but certainly from about 1790 it became the practice to take out all the pillars achieving an extraction of more than ninety per cent of the coal. The output for a single firm had risen from Halliwell's typical output of 7,846 tons in 1771 to outputs of around 50,000 tons per annum by the big firms such as Jarratt and Lofthouse, Hustler, Blundell, Clarke and German at the end of the century. Thus there must have been a great increase in the number of colliers employed in the pits there during the last two decades of the eighteenth century.

14 Ancient colliers' tools discovered in old workings at Dean Wood, Orrell

2.4 WINDING COAL

During the early part of our period there is no doubt that the windlass, jack roll, or turn, as it was known locally, would be used in some of the very shallow pits, but by 1750 the whim gin or whimsey was in common use in the district for winding coal.

All through Halliwell's Orrell Fire Engine Colliery accounts we find that as the sinking of each new shaft is completed and the pit 'eye' is opened out in the seam there is an allowance for 'setting up an engine called a whimsey'.

The carpenters bill for 1828 at Parbold Colliery included the following items:

	£	s	d
Gin wile [wheel] 85 feet of Timber at 2s 6d per foot	10	12	6
Hed gin Main bimon [beam] and poses [posts] 85 feet at 2s 6d per foot	10	12	6
Carpenters whork for the gin wile	5	0	0
Carpenters whork for the Hed Gin	2	0	0

This would probably be a small gin as the usual cost of a gin was £40 to £60. One example gives £57 as the cost of a gin, and a pair of ropes for it of 1½in diameter cost £9 and were said to last 16 to 18 months.

An early nineteenth century specification of a well-constructed gin gives the following particulars (Fig 15):

Drum Shaft: 13ft 6in long, 2ft 2in square, hooped and fitted with 2in diameter spindles at each end.

Span beam: 39ft long, 16in deep by 8in thick, supported by a triangular frame at each end, with bases 13ft long.

Horse arm: 35ft 8in long and 12in by 7in in section. This passed through a mortice in the drum shaft and was braced by 4in by 4in stays from the lower part of the drum shaft.

Drum: 9ft diameter by 2ft 6in deep, divided into two parts by a fillet in order to separate the ropes. Twelve horns at the top and the bottom prevented the ropes coming off. The lagging was made of elm.

Pit head frame: This was 24ft 6in from the gin frame. It was constructed of oak and was braced and stayed. Two 3ft diameter cast-iron pulleys were fitted directly over the pit shaft.

Jackanapes: Two large poles connected the gin frame and the pit head frame and carried the jackanapes or arms on which were mounted the friction rollers to keep the ropes straight.

Striking bar: This was fitted across the two uprights of the head frame. The banksman leaned on it when he drew the basket from the shaft on to the bank with a long iron hook.

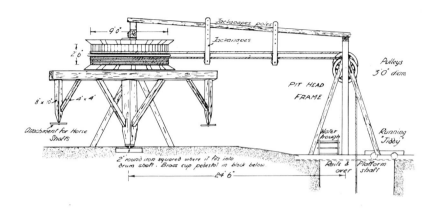

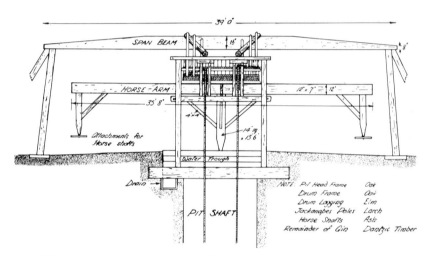

15 Whimsey or horse gin, from an 1842 design

Ropes were sometimes tarred or payed over with coarse canvas in order to preserve them, as they were a costly item. During some excavations in the 1920s a paved circular gin horse-walk about 30ft in diameter was uncovered at the site of one of Blundells' old pits in Orrell.

A plan of Clarke's leasehold dated 1810 shows a drawing of a whim gin which seems to show that they were still being used at that colliery at that time. At the time the Douglas was opened for navigation, at Sir Roger Bradshaigh's Curghey House Pit the whimsey was worked by four horses which trotted round a track four and three quarter times and travelled 151½yd to draw baskets from a pit 76½yd deep. From these figures the diameter of the rope drum is calculated to be 15.3ft and the diameter of the horse walk 34ft. Many horses were required as they had to work in relays, sometimes for only three or four hours each and spare horses always had to be in readiness in case one got injured or fell sick.

Newcomen steam pumping engines were sometimes used for winding in conjunction with overshot waterwheels by recirculating the waste water back onto the top of the wheel. These wheels had a double set of buckets for driving the wheel and rope drum attached to it in either direction. At the end of a wind the wooden trough or launder which fed the wheel was turned away from it by means of a lever and when it was required to wind in the opposite direction the trough was turned into the other set of buckets turning the wheel the other way. Although used in other parts of the Lancashire coalfield there is little evidence for their use in the Orrell area.

It is not clear when the Orrell colliery owners adopted the steam winding engine, but after 1780 many atmospheric engines were adapted for rotary motion by means of a crank, connecting rod and flywheel and some of these were used for winding coal. An excellent example of an atmospheric winding engine was erected at the William Pit at Whitehaven as late as 1806. In 1790-1 five winding engines of the Watt type (built in contravention of his patent, hence known as 'pirate' engines) were erected by John Wilkinson of Bersham and at least three of these were put to work in Lancashire. By 1795 Bateman and Sherratt of Salford had:

> improved upon and brought the steam engine to great perfection. Most of those that are used and set up in Manchester are of their make and fitting up. They are in general of a small size, very compact, stand in a small space, work smooth and easy and are scarcely heard in the building where erected. They are now used in cotton mills and for every purpose of the water wheel where a stream is not to be got and for winding up coals from a great depth in the coal pits which is performed with a quickness and ease not to be conceived.

This firm made both atmospheric and 'pirated' Watt engines. Watt's first winding engine was erected in 1784 but according to the lists of their engines in the Birmingham Reference Library they did not supply any winding engines to Lancashire.

About 1790 the steam-driven endless chain system of winding was introduced and was probably the method used at Blundell and Menzies' extensive Orrell Chain Colliery, which commenced in 1799, and at their Pemberton Chain Pit sunk in the 1820s. The Orrell Chain Colliery finished in 1820, so perhaps the same apparatus was transferred to Pemberton. This system was in use in East Lancashire until the end of the nineteenth century but with tubs instead of baskets:

> A small engine supplies the necessary motive power and by means of
> a chain drive and gearing, operates a pair of large sprocket wheels erect-
> ed vertically over the pit shaft. The sprocket wheels work what might
> be described as gigantic bicycle chains, each of course being endless and
> hanging vertically in the shaft and passing round pulleys at the bottom.
> The chains are kept steady by the pulleys which are, as a matter of
> fact, supported by the chains, the axles being free to move vertically
> in slide bars. At regular intervals, horizontal bars connect the two chains
> and to these bars the tubs are attached being suspended singly.

Gins were still in use in some of Blundells' pits in the early
nineteenth century. In a Pemberton Colliery Wages book for 1827
'R. White Gin driver at No 8 pit' is mentioned, which may have
been a reference to a sinking gin.

Apart from the beam engine, the engine most commonly used
for winding during the first half of the nineteenth century was the
single cylinder vertical steam engine with the drum mounted above
the cylinder on masonry pillars.

John Mildred Hustler erected both a beam winding engine (Fig
17) and a vertical winding engine at his new Orrell Colliery in
1846 and it is possible that these (or at least the beam engine)
were transferred from one of their older pits. This beam engine
was only broken up in 1907 and was described by Mr Moses
Ashurst the then manager of Orrell Colliery as having a cylinder
17in diameter with a stroke of 4ft, fitted with Watt's parallel
motion and driving a flywheel 15ft 6in diameter, with two sets
of cast iron 'verticals' or 'horns' 6ft 8in diameter. These were
specially made so that a flat winding rope could coil on itself
between the verticals set to the width of the rope. In this case the
rope was 3in x ½in. The wrought iron exhaust chimney was 18in
diameter and 18ft high and the engine house was 26ft long and
29ft wide. A 5in steam pipe connected the engine with the Cornish and egg-ended boilers. A cast-iron frame under the engine was
fixed to two massive ashlar stone pillars.

The vertical winding engine was built by Daglish and had a
34in diameter cylinder and a stroke of 5ft with Watt's parallel
motion and brass Cornish valves. The verticals were 14ft in diameter and the flywheel approximately 20ft diameter. It was also
fixed on very massive Ashlar foundations and beds. The engine
house consisted of brick with a stone parapet wall and was 19ft
by 17ft 6in. An 8ft diameter brick exhaust chimney was surmount-
ed by a wrought-iron chimney.

Flat hemp winding ropes had come into use about 1790. A
special drum slightly wider than the flat rope was used, on which

16 An endless-chain winding pit. Although taken at Bardsley Bridge, Ashton under Lyne, about 1868-72, this arrangement was similar to that used at Orrell (*L. Lees*)

the rope was coiled lap upon lap, being kept in position by verticals radiating from the shaft on each side of the drum. That these and flat wire ropes were in use at Pemberton is clear from Vol 11 of the *Mining Journal:*

> an early instance of the installation of flat wire ropes was at Pemberton Colliery, Lancs., where a pair of ropes were at work in September 1841, which was stated to have exceeded all expectations in the practice of winding and raising coal, and promised to be one of the finest inventions for working very deep mines ever yet discovered.

James Tonge, a Lancashire mining engineer recorded the common occurrence of shafts without guides or lining in 1850. It was also common practice for men and boys to stand in a small tub or basket suspended by chains from the end of a rope and requiring a careful balancing lest they fall out where there were no guides or conductors. The tub, during its slow descent or ascent, would be constantly turning round, having a tendency to make persons dizzy. Many cases have been known of them actually falling out

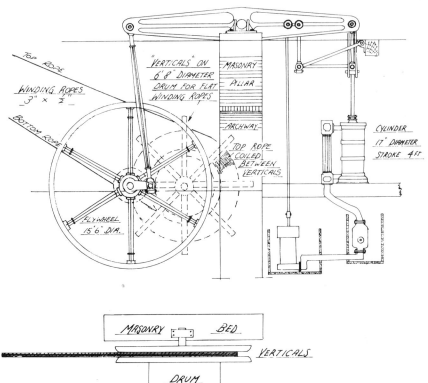

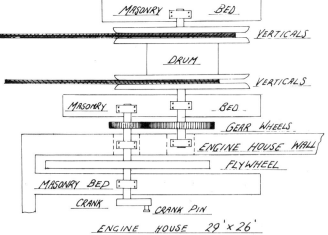

17 A reconstruction of Hustler's Orrell Colliery steam winding engine built in
    1846. Based on details left by Moses Ashurst, manager at the colliery. The
    plan shows details of the winding drum and 'verticals'

of the tub and being killed under such circumstances. At this time, however, at least some of the pits in the district were fitted with guide rods for the baskets as William Greener mentions 'taking the rods out of the Wood Pit' when that pit finished in 1858 and a stocktaking at Winstanley Colliery in 1845 mentions 'conductors' (guides) in the shafts.

2.5 UNDERGROUND WATER

The average rainfall in the Orrell district, is between 36in and 40in per annum. This represents 3,660 to 4,040 tons of water per statute acre a year and it has been estimated that one third, say 1,200 to 1,300 tons, of this percolates into the strata in every acre.

Since in Orrell large areas of the Five Feet Seam lay at very shallow depths, it was comparatively easy for water, especially storm water, to gain access to the workings as a consequence of the porosity of the surface rocks, which, being badly weathered, are open-jointed. Bad surface drainage also had an adverse effect by not carrying off the water to the brooks quickly enough during heavy rains.

For at least two centuries before the period we are considering, most of the mines in the Orrell belt had been drained by means of adit levels, which were known in Lancashire and surrounding counties as soughs. These were cross-measure drifts or tunnels, driven on a very slightly rising gradient from just above the highest flood water level of the lowest available and convenient stream, to intersect the seam or seams to be worked. From the point where the sough entered the seam, a water level or 'water lane' as they were known locally, was driven in the seam along the strike or level contour of the seam. Soughs varied in size but in the Orrell area they were rarely more than 4ft wide and indeed a sough that was opened up at Orrell House was 2ft 6in wide and 4ft 6in high with a narrow channel along the bottom of it. Such narrow drivages were occasioned by the proportionately lesser costs of excavation and the lesser likelihood of roof collapse. Similarly the water levels in the coal were seldom more than 4ft 6in wide and were protected from roof weights in the main body of the workings by ranges of pillars. Once the water lane was driven, coal-drawing or whimsey shafts were sunk to or alongside it at regular intervals, so that all the coal between the water lane and the outcrop or previous rise workings was readily available for working. The coal remained free of water troubles as long as the water lane and sough were kept in good condition. This system was used from the sixteenth century onwards in the northern portion of Orrell and UpHolland, adjacent to the deep ravine of Dean Wood and the River Douglas and in those parts of Orrell, Winstanley and Pemberton lying contiguous to Smithy Brook between the former Red Wood near Edge Hall farmhouse and through the Pingot to Rylands Mill bridge at Pony Dick.

The colliery operated by the Bankes family which worked the Orrell Five Feet Seam between the Pingot and the outcrop west of Winstanley Park cricket ground and Atherton (formerly Ashton's) Farm was typical of the local system. Here the coal lay at a depth of 60ft or less over most of this area, and in Clarke's Engine Pit in the Pingot sunk in the 1790s it was only 22ft deep. In No 2 or Nicholson's Pit on the hill it was 60ft deep.

In the first development in the sixteenth century, short open trenches and soughs were driven into the seam to dewater narrow belts of coal near the crop. As these shallow areas became exhausted, it became necessary to start a new sough from a point lower down the brook. This meant of course that the soughs became progressively longer. In 1573 it was agreed between James Worsley of Worsley Mesnes in Pemberton and Edmund Winstanley of Winstanley that a sough should be made to drain their respective coal mines in the Red Wood or Captain's Clough area. Later soughs here were the joint efforts of the successors of James Worsley and Edmund Winstanley, the Downes family of Wardley and the Bankes family of Winstanley respectively. In 1625 William Bankes entered into negotiations with the Birchall family of Orrell regarding the construction of a sough to drain their mines.

The position in the eighteenth century was that there was an ancient sough in the Pingot, which had been driven at the joint expense of the Bankes and Downes families. For many years it was cleaned out and repaired by Bankes's workmen and by those of Mr Downes and his successors, Lord Colchester and Earl Rivers. By the mid-eighteenth century the Pingot sough was not maintained since all the coal, or as much as the owners cared to work, was got in the Downes estate. In the meantime, William Bankes was working the coal away from and to the rise of the sough towards what is now the site of Winstanley Park cricket ground. Presumably he was not troubled with water for a long period and the water continued to find its way through the sough. Eventually the sough became blocked because the miller of Rylands Mill damned the water in it for a dry weather supply to his mill. But 'the water occassioned the mettle [shale strata] to melt and fall down which stopped the water running in its usual course through the fault'.

A large area of coal remained to the dip of the water level connected with the sough, the level being approximately 193ft OD. No doubt the surveyor who advised William Bankes (perhaps Richard Melling the Wigan surveyor and engineer) made levellings along Smithy Brook and arrived at the conclusion that it was possible to drain almost all the dip coal down to the Tinker Hole Fault in the Pingot by driving a sough from a point on the brook near Rylands Corn Mill to intersect the Orrell Five Feet Seam through the Tinker Hole Fault under the wood now known as the New Covert (Figs 18 and 19).

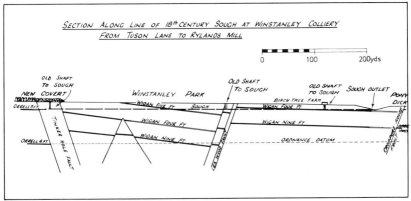

18   Section along William Bankes's sough at Winstanley

However, in order to work this coal, it was advisable to dewater the 'Old Drowned Hollows' on the rise side of the old Pingot sough level and attempts were made to clear the sough but there was much blackdamp in it and the workmen 'did not care to go in'. The water finally got vent, due presumably to the increasing head of water as the workings went to the rise and it 'boiled up in a strong stream known as the Boiling Pingot until 1756'. After this a new branch of the sough was driven which apparently successfully dewatered the old works.

The entrance to the ancient sough was at the side of Smithy Brook, half way down the old Winstanley Colliery sidings. It was 1,200 feet long with four shafts for ventilation and winding out the debris made in driving the sough. The new branch was 520ft in length and its junction with the original sough was at a distance of 750ft from the mouth. There were five winding and ventilation shafts and a dam in the branch.

19 Outlet of William Bankes's sough

Hawarden, working the Five Feet Seam on the Pemberton side of the Pingot, drove a sough 700ft long with its entrance near the old sough but apparently it was not a successful venture as it was described as a 'new dry sough'. There were three sough pits along its length.

The 2,250ft long sough driven from Rylands Mill began at a level of 168ft OD and entered the Orrell Five Feet Seam at approximately 180ft OD. It is still functioning, draining the modern Summersales Colliery workings under Winstanley Park. There were only three known shafts for ventilation and winding, one under Birch Tree Farm barn, a second one in the field between the Delph Plantation and the New Covert, the third on the western edge of the New Covert. The sough was 102ft deep in the second shaft which was sunk almost on the 40yd Lea Wood Fault which throws the measures down west. This sough was 4ft square in section where it was driven through rock, and in the short length where it crossed the Wigan Five Feet Seam it was 2ft 6in wide and 4ft 6in high.

Near the brook at Rylands Mill it entered the hard sandstone known as the Wigan Four Feet Rock and just beyond the second shaft it crossed the Lea Wood Fault and the Wigan Five Feet Seam and soon afterwards entered the Wigan Five Feet Rock, a hard yellow sandstone. The hardness of this sandstone may be judged from Winstanley Park wall, the stone of which was quarried from this bed.

From the point where the sough met the Tinker Hole Fault it was driven over 300ft through a shatter belt. The extremely hard physical labour involved in driving this sough can hardly be imagined today. Even with the assistance of gunpowder, which was costly and used sparingly, it could not have been anything but difficult as it would be an arduous job drilling horizontal holes by hand in stone as hard as the Wigan Five Feet and Wigan Four Feet Rock. There must have been many mis-shots causing much frustration. The length through the Tinker Hole shatter belt would be difficult to support where it crossed through fault 'listing' — a soapy clay substance, especially when wet. Soughs were sometimes bricked and arched through bad ground such as this and indeed the nearby water tunnel from Blundells' Venture Pit to the Pemberton Engine Pit was walled and arched with stone where it crossed the Croppers House Fault zone.

The difficulty of keeping the sough open along this stretch is suggested by a condition in the 1792 lease of William Bankes to Clarke and German of the Orrell Four Feet Seam underlying the Five Feet workings, requiring them to keep his workings dry by means of their fire engine. The water made in the Five Feet was quite considerable amounting on average to 13,200 gallons an hour.

In the accounts of Winstanley Collieries in the 1760s there is a regular weekly payment for the driving of the sough in connection with the pits in the Tuson Lane area, and this no doubt referred to the Rylands Mill sough. In 1872 Thomas Fairhurst, an old employee at Winstanley Collieries made the following statement about the Rylands Mill sough and the underground waterways to the River Douglas:

In reference to the old colliery workings by the late William Bankes Esq., there were several old pits in the Salterley Woods which were left, it appears for the water to find its way through from the old workings in pits near the Gardens in the Orrell Five Feet mine.
In connection with this in the Salterley Wood there is a Tunnel driven commencing in the brook near Rylands Mill going from there into the pits above named. This tunnel it appears was driven for the purpose of taking all the water made in the workings away, leaving them entirely dry and which has been cleaned out from time to time to keep the water course clear. There are also some pits in the New Cover that were left open by Clarkes in connection with the Clarke & Co's colliery. There is a very large quantity of water runs down the pit near William Nicholson's top end of Cover from workings chiefly at the outcrop in the ditch at the bottom end of Chair Nursery, going through all the old workings by Clark and Co. both in the townships of Winstanley and Orrell and comes out into the River Douglas near Dean Locks on the Leeds and Liverpool Canal. This information was given by Thomas Fairhurst in the presence of M. Bankes Esq. and taken down by George Holland underlooker to M. Bankes Esq. at the collieries.

Thomas Fairhurst was referring to the fact that long after all the Orrell belt collieries finished, the old soughs and water tunnels continued to operate and kept the underground water of the whole of the belt down to just above the level of the Douglas at Gathurst.

The water in Clarkes' Four Feet workings rose to a line between Atherton Farm and Gorsey Cottage on the west side of the M6 motorway at 91ft 6in OD. There was a connection with the Orrell Four Feet workings by J. Blundell and Son under the Duke of Bridgewater's Winstanley Estate and Sir Robert Holt Leigh's Edge Hall Estate. At the point where the water level reached the Grand Dyke Fault, a water tunnel had been driven by Blundells to connect with their Slycroft Colliery Five Feet workings, which, owing to the 64yd throw of the fault, were on the same level as the Four Feet on the Winstanley side of the fault. At this point, a water pit had been sunk down to the Slycroft Colliery Four Feet to take the water down to the pumping engine there. When this ceased to work, however, in about 1830, the water filled up all the workings between Slycroft at Far Moor and Clarke's and Hustler's workings near Orrell Post, along with both Blundells' Chain and Orrell House collieries, to the level of the two water tunnels connecting Blundells' Chain Colliery with Orrell House Colliery workings. The level of these tunnels was 96ft OD and the Orrell House workings were drained by a long sough to Dean Locks, the outlet of which was 87ft OD. It was reported in 1872 by Thomas Millard Reade, a civil engineer, that a large volume of water flowed from this sough into the Douglas.

These old soughs, tunnels and waterways are now blocked and the water has risen in the old workings and shafts under the west side of Winstanley Park and Orrell to a level of approximately 200ft OD. The eighteenth century sough which drained Ayrefield Colliery Four Feet workings into Dean Brook was open for a considerable distance until the early twentieth century. It was approximately 4ft high by 4ft wide, but at the mouth it was between 5ft and 6ft wide. In 1872 it was reported that ochre water was seen flowing out of old soughs draining the Five Feet Seam into Dean Brook. Halliwell stated in June 1759 that he had spent more than £200 on driving a sough to Orrell Hall demesnes Five Feet from low lying land belonging to Thomas Owen. He paid a yardage rate of 2s 8d for a sough of this kind.

Soughs were costly to drive and maintain and where the make of water was not excessive and the shafts were shallow, it was sometimes possible to keep the water down by winding it out with tubs or barrels, either during the night shift from a coal drawing shaft or during the day shift from a special water pit. The winding

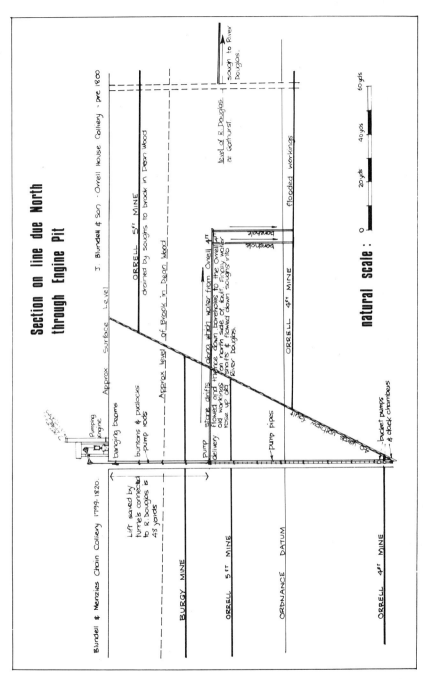

20 Section through Blundells' Chain Colliery Engine Pit, showing water tunnels and boreholes

77

apparatus was the 'turn' or whimsey, exactly as for coal drawing. Winding water out of a shaft has been a fairly common method of dealing with water up to modern times. For example, Armstrong of Newcastle, Blundells' consultant mining engineer, advised them in 1853 to discontinue with the pumping engine at their Tan House Pits and as

> little water is found in these seams, a tank worked by the winding engine and made to discharge itself may be introduced at night to remove the days accumulation.

The same shaft was used from 1877 until early in the twentieth century solely for winding water of the new Winstanley Collieries sunk by Meyrick Bankes the younger, a connection to it having been made after it was discontinued for coal production by Blundells in 1873. The tanks were fitted with two clacks in the bottom for filling and one in the side at the bottom for emptying, the latter being connected by a rod to a lever protruding from the side of the tank. On reaching the pit bank the lever caught a tripwire, lifting the clack and emptying the tank.

After an inrush of water into Blundells' New Venture Pit on 19 April 1913 two 350 gallon tanks were attached to the winding ropes and, with the water at a depth of 98yd, they were capable of raising 388 gallons per minute.

There are many references in eighteenth century colliery accounts to the purchase of buckets, tubs or barrels for winding water. John Taylor of Newburgh specialised in the making of these early in the nineteenth century and charged £2 each for them.

Water winding shafts were sunk at the extreme dip side of the coal area to be worked, water levels being driven out from them on each side. The water from the higher side workings ran down into the water levels and from there into the 'dib hole' of the shaft. This was an extension of the shaft for several yards below the seam level, formed to act as a standage for the water. Contemporary colliery accounts show many entries of payments made for 'cleaning out the dib hole' as sludge and other debris accumulated in it. In the two weeks ending 16 October 1829 Thomas Coston was paid 3s at Parbold Colliery for 'cleaning dibhole two times at 1/6d per'.

A means of raising water which was becoming obsolete in mines by the middle of the eighteenth century was the chain of buckets. This consisted of one or two endless chains hanging down the shaft and worked by a sprocket drum on a long axle over the top of the shaft, the axle generally receiving its motion from a waterwheel or a horse gin. At the bottom of the shaft the chain went round another sprocket drum which served to keep it in position. Buckets were suspended at intervals, either from a single chain or from pins between two chains. The buckets 'are made sometimes as barrels, some of strong leather, others of boards nailed together'. The more efficient buckets were fitted with a clack in the bottom so as to fill with water more quickly.

Another form of endless-chain pump known as the rag and chain pump (Fig 21) was in common use in the collieries. In this type, one leg of the endless chain ran through a pipe, generally not more than 5in diameter. Secured at intervals to the chain and fastened round it were balls equal in diameter to the pipe, made of pieces of leather sewn together and stuffed with rags or horsehair. These ascended the pipe and forced the water up in front of them. Rag and chain pumps were worked either by waterwheels or horse gins. The barrel of one of these pumps discovered locally is now in the Blackburn Museum. A 5in diameter pump driven at a speed of 200ft per minute would lift 10,200 gallons per hour, and would require 4hp to lift this quantity by 80ft. Assuming an efficiency of fifty per cent, including slip, eight horses would be required to work the machine.

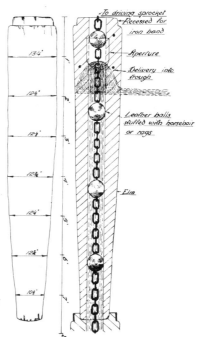

21 A rag and chain pump, found at
    Cherry Tree near Blackburn. Now
    in Blackburn Museum

Elm or oak pipes known as 'pumps or stocks' were in common use in mines until the middle of the eighteenth century (although they were used for wells for a hundred years after this), but they were gradually replaced by cast iron pipes. As early as 1727 an estimate for a Newcomen engine erected by the Quakers John and Henry Fidoe to dewater their mines at Wednesbury in South Staffordshire had the following item 'Pumps of cast iron will weigh about 45 cwts at 30s per cwt equals £67 10s'. A note at the bottom of the estimate says 'if you have wood pumps it will lessen the first charge about £20'. Wooden pumps were still being used in 1760 when the Newcomen engine at Lye, Stourbridge was erected as, although cast iron windbores, pump barrels and clack chambers were fitted, elm trees were used for the pipe above the working barrel in the shaft.

The craftsmen who made wooden pumps were very skilled. It was said that it took nine hours to bore a 16ft oak log. They were bored on two trestles by two men with long shanked shell augers weighing about 56lb and working simultaneously from each end. Shell augers were used as screw-pointed augers were said to follow the grain and never ran true. The holes were cut in by a gouge for about 1in deep before the auger could be used. Sighting strings on nails and plumb bobs were used to set the line of the augers properly. The joints were of the spigot and faucet type. The spigot was formed simply by tapering one end of the pipe and the faucet end was cut out to receive the spigot of the next pipe. The faucet was generally banded with a ring of iron flat.

When these pipes were fixed in the shaft, the system was generally to have the spigot uppermost. Around this was wrapped a piece of flannel or similar material which had been dipped in boiling tallow mixed with resin and whiting, and the faucet end of the next pipe was guided onto it as it was lowered from above.

The rag and chain may have been the type of pump installed by Edward Holme at his Orrell Colliery in 1710, on the other hand it is more likely to have been a bucket lift pump.

The pumps in Halliwell's first Engine Pit in Orrell sunk in the Orrell Hall desmesnes in 1763, would appear to have been worked by a waterwheel situated on or near Ackhurst Brook which flows past the present Leigh Cottage. Although there were a number of baskets of coal allowed for the engine this is booked as 'customs for the engine, hiring men, waydrawing, dressing, smiths fire etc'. and the colliery was then known as the Orrell Hall Colliery. After 1769 however, Halliwell's colliery is referred to as Orrell Fire Engine Colliery and the accounts of the colliery show that coal was supplied to the engine boiler fire.

Halliwell had previous experience of waterwheel driven pumps. He set one up at his engine pit in Aspull and in 1746 carried out a test on the 'Great Wheel's performance'. The pumps worked by the wheel were bucket lift pumps and they raised 9 gallons each stroke from a depth of 58yds and worked at a speed of 7 strokes a minute. This is 3,780 gallons per hour, equivalent to 3.3hp.

A letter dated 30 October 1769 from John Jackson of Orrell House shows how unreliable waterwheels were in dry weather. Jackson's pits were flooded because there had been little rain and there was not sufficient water in the brooks to work the wheel:

> I hear you are told I have got your coals in the deyn which you may easily be incensed by sending Peter Rigby or any other knowing person into our works so soon as the water is out, but we are sure we are forty yards from your coals and cannot be able to get nearer until I have been at the charge of sinking so as to fix a poomp or have the water laded by scope and as we shall so soon as any quantity of rain falls to play the water out by the Engine begin and get the said coal that lyes adjoining yours which will be the means to lay yours dry. You may have an opportunity of getting yours by the same means as we must use and shall be willing to assist you therein or any other mine you care to gate so farr as in my power lyes by the virtue of my Engine etc.

About the middle of the eighteenth century the engineer John Smeaton carried out experiments with models of waterwheels and was able to greatly improve their efficiency. As to the most suitable type of wheel for a given situation, he said

> Where the fall of water is between four and ten feet a breast wheel should be erected provided there be enough of water; an undershot wheel should be used where the fall was below four feet, and an overshot wheel where it exceeds ten feet. Alternately in the latter case the fall could be divided in two and two breast wheels erected upon it.

Dependence on the vagaries of the weather was the greatest drawback to waterwheels and windmills, and in some cases horse-driven pumping engines were installed either as standbys for use in dry periods or as the main pumping engine. They were very expensive in running costs owing to the large number of horses required. These were employed in relays of two or four horses depending on the height the water had to be lifted and on the number of bucket lifts worked. Strong horses, expensive to buy, were required for this heavy duty and spare ones were kept in readiness. John Halliwell stated that he had lift pumps worked by horses and wheels and 'it was very trouble sum having so many pumps, or else the pit was a good bargain and the men got money enufe'.

An interesting example of the cost of a horse-driven engine was given by Dr Thomas Hawarden who, in the late 1750s was working the Orrell Five Feet Seam north of the Pingot where the Triangle Valve Co offices are now situated. A short time before, this land had been purchased by Alexander Leigh from Mathew and John Lyon who had just bought it from Lady Penelope Cholmondeley, the heiress of the Downes estate. William Bankes had given Hawar - den permission to erect a weir to convey water to the waterwheel at his nearby Engine Pit. This arrangement only ran smoothly for a short time and in 1760, Hawarden sued Bankes for diverting the water from his pumping engine and thus causing part of his mine to flood. He was forced to erect a horse engine and although this, with repairs from 22 May 1758 to 29 December 1759, cost only £63 2s 0½d (£63.10) the running costs were very high: 'Working the Horse Engine with four horses and two drivers from 3rd July 1758 to 1st Jan 1760 being 19 months at £12. 12s 0d. per month amounts to £239. 8s. 0d'.

Smeaton designed some excellent examples of this kind of pump. One of these erected as late as 1780, although not at a colliery, gives a good impression of what they were like. It had a horse-arm 33ft long secured to a main vertical shaft 2ft 6in diameter on which was a 20ft diameter horizontal cogged wheel driving a vertical pinion 2ft 6in diameter. The pinion shaft was 12ft in length and 10in diameter and at the opposite end to the pinion there was a 10ft diameter flywheel and a crank working a 17ft 6in long rock-ing beam through a connecting rod 24ft long. The shaft-pump spear rods were suspended from the opposite end of the beam.

2.6 THE FIRE ENGINES OF ORRELL

Considerable feeders of water were met with in opening out the Lower or Four Feet Seam in Orrell and Winstanley and it is quite certain that it could not have been worked without the aid of the Newcomen and Cornish beam pumping engines installed there from 1769 onwards. These steam pumping engines were so very essential to the winning of the deeper seam that a description of their development is of interest.

Thomas Savery (1650-1715) had patented in 1698, a machine with no moving parts except the valves, intended for the 'Raising of Water by the Impellent Force of Fire', which he said would 'be of great use and Advantage for Drayning Mines'. The working of Savery's pump has been described as follows:

Steam from a boiler was admitted into a closed vessel and there condensed by cold water being poured on the outside. The resulting vacuum
drew the water up the suction pipe through a non-return valve in the
bottom of the vessel. When steam was again admitted, the water was
driven out of the vessel through a second non-return valve and up the
delivery pipe. The steam and cold water valves were worked by hand.

Savery's final design consisted of two boilers and two chambers.
Unfortunately, it was incapable of a total lift of more than about
50ft. Therefore it was of little use in all but very shallow mines
and for that very reason it could have been successfully applied
in the shallow flat-lying Orrell Five Feet Seam in the area where
sough drainage was not possible, but nothing is known of any such
application. In theory several lifts in series could have been used
for the drainage of deeper mines and in fact this was done in sinking pits in the late nineteenth century with the successor of Savery's
pump, the Pulsometer. This was a double-chambered pump which
worked in exactly the same way as Savery's, except that the steam
was at a much higher pressure. Condensation occured when the
water was depressed by the steam to the top of the delivery passage, and when the steam attempted to rush through the opening
it violently agitated the surface of the water, causing instant condensation.

A large Pulsometer installed in 1887 was still in use in connection with the trough-washer at Blundells' Pemberton Colliery until
the 1920's. If for any reason the pump would not work, the pump-
man always reverted to Savery's original method of pouring cold
water over the outside of the chamber in order to create a vacuum
and get it going. The pump body was made of gunmetal, a replacement costing £500 at the beginning of this century. The great advantage of this kind of pump was its capacity to pump very dirty
water, hence its widespread use as a return pump for washery
water. The Pulsator and the Aqua Thruster pumps also worked on
Savery's principle.

However, the engine that came into common use at Orrell and
throughout Britain as a pumping engine was the type invented by
Thomas Newcomen (1663-1729). It was far more successful than
Savery's and was the first reciprocating steam engine. It consisted
of an open-topped vertical cylinder, fitted with a piston connected
by a piston rod or rods and chains to an overhead pivoted beam,
of large cross-section and generally of oak. At its other end the
beam was connected, again by chains, to the wooden spear rods
which worked the series of bucket lifts in the pit shaft. Each end
of the beam was fitted with a segment or 'arch-head' to which the
chains were secured.

When the engine was at rest, the weight of the spear rods pushed the buckets in the shaft pumps down to the bottom of the stroke and lifted the engine piston to the top of its stroke. To get it in motion steam was admitted into the cylinder on the underside of the piston, the air in the cylinder being blown out by the steam through a pipe known as the 'snift' which was fitted with a non-return valve. The steam in the cylinder was then quickly condensed by cold water, injected through a pipe into the bottom of the cylinder, from a tank high in the engine house. This caused a partial vacuum in the cylinder and the pressure of the atmosphere then pushed the piston down to the bottom of its stroke drawing up the spear rods, thus causing the buckets to lift the water up the rising main in the pit shaft. The injection valve was then closed and the steam valve between the boiler and the cylinder was opened. The steam blew the air out through the snift and the hot water left in the cylinder was expelled through another pipe called the eduction pipe which was also fitted with a non-return valve and connected with a cylinder of water several feet below the engine cylinder. On the admission of the steam the vacuum was destroyed, the weight of the spear rods drew the piston to the top of the cylinder and the cycle recommenced.

The steam and injection valves were reopened and shut automatically by the 'working gear' which was operated by pegs in a wooden 'plug rod' or 'plug tree' hung from the beam. However, to set the engine in motion, the tappets of the working gear were operated by hand by the engineman for several strokes. Cold water for the injection cistern was pumped up to it by a piston pump known as the jack head pump worked from the main beam. A collar of oakum was sometimes used as packing for the piston rod where it worked through the top cover of this pump.

For many years, only one boiler was used and this was placed immediately below the cylinder, but towards the end of the eighteenth century as larger and larger engines were built, two or even four boilers were set up for a single engine. No information has come to light on the places of manufacture of the early fire engines in Orrell. Up to 1759 when the Carron Works in Scotland began boring cylinders with Smeaton's improved boring mill, many cast-iron cylinders were supplied by the great Coalbrookdale works in Shropshire. Brass cylinders had been in use earlier on, especially in the Northern coalfield but by the time Halliwell erected Orrell's first Fire Engine in 1769, it had become standard practice to use cast-iron cylinders, iron founding and engine manufacture having come a long way since Newcomen's day. Other engine parts such as the valves also came from Coalbrookdale, but many of the parts

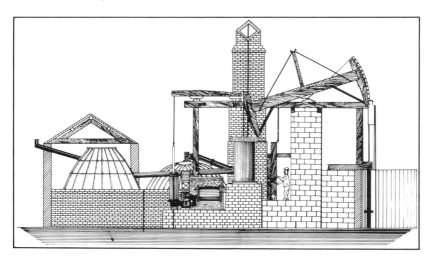

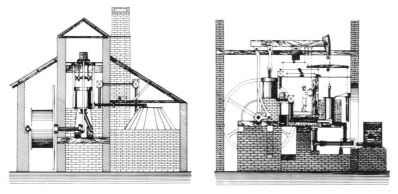

22 Atmospheric pumping and winding engines typical of those used in most coalfields in the late-eighteenth and early-nineteenth centuries. These were in use at Whitehaven in 1806

were obtained locally. There were several iron forges and brass foundries in the area, Brock Mill Forge at Haigh and Pepper Mill Brass Foundry at Wigan being two examples. Apart from the cylinder, much of the engine work was within the capabilities of a good carpenter, blacksmith and plumber. The skill of Lancashire mechanics was well known and there is no doubt that once they had made themselves familiar with the fire engine, they would not need outside help in erecting and maintaining them. When London's first Newcomen engine was erected in 1725 at York Buildings Water Works, one of the engineers in charge was described as a 'Lancashire Wizzard with long black hair and a grim visage'. Long before the Orrell engines were erected fire engines were at work in collieries at Prescot and St Helens.

In his book published in London in 1792, Adam Walker says

> Wigan has produced many excellent self-taught mechanics. Dick Melling simplified the steam engine, gave the windmill an equitable motion and the means of turning itself round. His bucket engine drained a valuable cannel mine for many years at small expense and many other contrivances of his challenge equal merit in simplicity and effect. Indeed the machinery necessary in such coal works has called forth the genius and invention of many more mechanics that do honour to human abilities.

John Wilkinson of Bersham near Wrexham set up his patent boring mill in 1775 and this was a great improvement on all its predecessors because the boring bar was held firmly at both ends in lathe chucks, whereas all previous boring bars, intended mainly for boring cannon, were only secured at one end and did not produce a true cylinder. Just before that date in 1769, however, Watt had taken out patents for a separate condenser, steam jacket and closed-top cylinder, Wilkinson supplying the cylinder for Watt's first successful pumping engine at Bloomfield Colliery in South Staffordshire. Bateman and Sherratt of Salford was another successful firm of engine makers in the 1780s and 1790s and along with Wilkinson and others they were accused of supplying engines of Watt's improved design and thus infringing his patent. Joshua Wrigley of Manchester and Francis Thompson of Ashover in Derbyshire were also well-known builders of fire engines during this period, but there is no evidence that they supplied any engine to the Orrell colliery owners.

A list of engines built by John Wilkinson between 1776 and 1795 sent by James Watt Junior to his father does not include any of the Orrell engines, but mentions two supplied to collieries near St Helens.

However, there is an account extant for the building of a fire engine at the Kirkless Cannel Pits at Ince on the north-east side of Wigan in 1773 and the following items show that the main parts of this were made by Wilkinson at Bersham:

July 31 1773	To P. Rigby expenses to going to Bersham about ye engine 4 days horse and self	£1. 2. 6d.
Nov 20	Carting engine from Chester, part of it	£5. 4. 0d.
Dec 31	Carriage of parts of ye engine	£1. 8. 0d.

Feb 1   Paid J. Wilkinson & Co for
             cylinder   £208. 8. 0d.

The Engine Beam, pulley blocks, snatch blocks and three legs were carted from Liverpool, 'Pan plates' for the boiler, brass cocks, lead work, iron and steel, chains, leather etc were purchased locally and all necessary smiths work and carpentry work were carried out on the spot.

The engine first worked on December 18th 1774 when £2 11s 6d was spent on ale for the workmen in celebration of that event.

In 1789 plans were on foot at Haigh Ironworks, Wigan to out-strip Wilkinson by erecting a 'boring mill which I now venture to say shall not be equalled by any in the kingdom'. In September of the following year, the following advertisement appeared in *Gore's General Advertiser,* a Liverpool newspaper:

> The Hon Robert Lindsay & Co announce they have erected a Blast furnace and Boring Mill at Haigh offer services in the Foundry business. Having engaged Engineers and able workmen they are enabled to under-take the complete construction of Fire Engines of every kind .

Again in 1811 a circular tells us that the works had long been in the habit of making fire engines, every description of machinery and all manner of castings. It is very probable that most of the Orrell engines erected after 1790 were built at Haigh, for example the 84in engine purchased by Blundells for their Pemberton Engine Pit in 1820, but unfortunately no accounts survive. Thirty-two years later, Haigh Ironworks built the world's largest engine for Mostyn Colliery in North Wales. This was known as *Dee Engine,* with a piston 100in diameter and a stroke of 14ft.

Although Watt's engine saved up to two-thirds of the fuel used by the Newcomen engine, this was not too important in the case of collieries, as small coal was for the most part unsaleable and there was plenty of it available for the colliery fire engines. Smeaton, in a letter to Watt dated 15 Feb 1778 said he had no doubt 'your scheme will answer a very valuable End where coals are Dear; And be of little consequence upon the Coal pitt Hill'. The great advantage of Watt's engine was the economy in steam resulting from the cylinder being kept continuously hot and the condenser contin-uously cool. In the case of the Newcomen engine the cylinder was alternately heated and cooled.

The Cornish engine was developed from the Watt single acting engine, but it was worked expansively by high pressure steam. The later Orrell beam engines were probably of the Cornish type, the one set up by John Mildred Hustler in 1846 at his new Orrell Colliery at Walthew House certainly was, as in all probability was

Woodcock and Haliburton's engine at Lamberhead Green. This commenced work two years after Blundells' Pemberton engines, which were of the Cornish type.

The Cornish engine did not differ greatly in appearance from the Newcomen type except that the cylinder top was fitted with a cap and glands for the piston rod to work through. The piston rod was connected to the beam by Watt's patent parallel motion and the condenser and air pump were separate, although some of the late eighteenth century Newcomen engines were fitted with small separate 'pickle pot' condensers. The steam-jacketed cylinder was generally encased in wood, the annular space between the two being filled with sawdust and the whole enclosed by brickwork plastered on the outside. The cylinder cover was fitted with a false lid or cap which enclosed a thick layer of sawdust to protect it from the cooling influence of the air. The space under the cylinder bottom was protected from the same influence by steam filling it from the steam jacket pipe.

Cast iron beams, sometimes solid, but often in two halves bolted together, with distance blocks in between to keep them parallel, had been introduced about 1801 for both Watt and Newcomen engines. Watt had seldom used steam above 7 lb/in^2 pressure, but after his patent expired in 1800, steam pressures were gradually increased up to 35 or 40 lb/in^2.

All these pumping engines and their associated pitwork were very costly. John Curr, manager at the Duke of Norfolk's Sheffield Collieries gave the following figures in 1797:

| | Engine with cylinder diameter of: | | | |
	30"	40"	50"	60"
Cost of sinking engine pit and fitting 2 bucket pumps complete with pipes buntons and all other pitwork and shear legs at the surface etc.	£328	£609	£858	£1185
Cost of Engine and Engine House	£600	£827	£1146	£1556
Total	£928	£1431	£2004	£2741

A price list dated 5 Dec 1815 shows again how very costly steam engines were at that time:

Power of steam engines and their price received from Messrs James Lindsay and Co of Wigan near Liverpool.

Haigh Ironworks near Wigan, Lancs. Powers of condensing steam engines upon the best principle of the best materials and workmanship adapted either for rotative motion or for pumping complete to the first motion with preparation for connecting the pumps or wheels.

4 horse power complete		£300
6 ,, ,,		£400
8 ,, ,,		£500
10 ,, ,,		£580
12 ,, ,,		£630
16 ,, ,,		£800
20 ,, ,,		£1000
26 ,, ,,		£1200
30 ,, ,,		£1320
36 ,, ,,		£1500
40 ,, ,,		£1630
46 ,, ,,		£1750
50 ,, ,,		£1870

Delivered in Liverpool

N.B. Intermediate powers in proportion.

Some of the local pumping engines were of much greater horse-power than is shown in the above list and therefore the prices would be higher still. For example Blundells' 84in engine at Pemberton built at Haigh Ironworks in 1820 was 200hp.

In a paper given to the Manchester Geological Society in October 1840, Sir William Fairbairn, the engineer, had this to say of the Cornish engine which had by that time reached its peak of development:

The Cornish Engine as now constructed, is what is technically called single acting, that is, the force of the steam is applied on one side of the piston only, and that during the time of lifting the load. On the outstroke, or during the descent of the plungers and pump rods, the steam (after it has performed the lift) is admitted from the upper to the lower side of the piston and the pressure being equal, the return stroke is effected by the preponderance of the weight in the pit.

Suppose the steam engine to have terminated the return stroke, everything at rest, and the piston in that quiescent state ready to commence the lift. In such a position, a rush of high pressure steam is suddenly produced, the inertia of the load in the pit is overcome and motion ensues. This motion would, however, soon terminate but for the expansive action which takes place when the communication between the cylinder and the boiler (now open) is suddenly cut off. This is done at a very early period of the piston's motion, by rapidly closing the steam valve, and thus excluding the further admission of steam, and retaining only a small volume (probably not more than one sixth of the contents of the cylinder) to urge forward the piston and terminate the stroke.

At first sight this force would scarcely appear adequate to the immense load which has to be raised; but on further examination we shall find the process and likewise the contrivances for these objects equally ingenious and effective. Having overcome the vis inertia of the mass, it will be found that the remainder of the stroke is duly effected by the steam's expansive action, and the consequent enlargement of its volume to the end of its stroke.

At the termination of the stroke, the equilibrium valve opens and the steam — now greatly attenuated, is admitted from the upper to the lower side of the piston, and the pressure being equal on both sides, the return stroke is performed in equilibrio by the weight of the pump rods as they descend in the pit.

When the retrograde motion takes place, it will be observed that the steam in the cylinder having expanded to five or six times its bulk, is greatly reduced in pressure, and the force being no longer equal to the resistance, the return stroke must of necessity take place as soon as the equilibrium valve effects a communication between the top and the bottom of the cylinder.

From this it is clear that the return stroke will be made with the velocity due to the weight in the pit; its accelerated motion might be attended with danger if it were not counteracted by the equilibrium valve, which shuts before the termination of the stroke, and retains a portion of steam between the piston and the cylinder cover. This steam is forcibly compressed as the piston ascends, operates as an elastic cushion to receive the shock against the cylinder cover.

The cataract governor, invented by Watt, controlled the speed of the engines. It consisted of a small forcing pump placed in a circular tank of water. The speed of this pump was controlled by the engineman as he could regulate the size of the pump outlet passage by means of a plug. By a series of rods and weights this pump controlled the opening first of the exhaust and then of the steam valve, thus causing the engine to commence the next down stroke.

Before 1800 the boilers to raise steam for these engines would be of the old 'haystack' or 'beehive' type originally constructed of copper, but during the second half of the eighteenth century boilers of wrought iron plates riveted together, generally with hemp rope packing between the joints, were introduced. Another common type used in the latter part of the eighteenth century was the 'wagon' boiler introduced by James Watt. All these were heated on their undersides, which were concave to prevent the accumulation of deposit and provided with flues on what was termed the 'wheeldraught' system. The heated gases passed under the boiler, rose up one side-flue, passed round the back and along the other side-flue and so to the chimney.

About 1800 the egg-ended boiler 5-6ft in diameter and 20-35ft long was introduced by the Cornish engineer Woolf, but before this time Watt was partial to the cast iron boiler with large water tubes incorporated in it. In 1806 Trevithick introduced the Cornish boiler, long and cylindrical with a single internal flue and furnace.

The principal difference between the pumps and pit work of the Newcomen and Cornish engines was that the former worked bucket lift pumps, whereas the latter could work both lift pumps and forcing pumps. Usually, however, Cornish pumping engines worked a bucket or duplicate buckets in the lowest lift and plungers or rams in the higher lifts. The reason for using a bucket lift in the bottom set was so that in the event of trouble, when the water in the shaft rose above the clack or the bucket, these could be drawn up to a clack door higher in the range or drawn out of the pipe altogether, and be replaced, whereas a ram would be drowned and out of reach.

Within living memory the 20in bucket from the 'Big Lift' (as Blundells' Cornish engine at Pemberton was known) was many times drawn out of the stocks, wound up the pit by the 'jack engine' and put in a pit tub which was drawn by a pony to the 'shops', where it was fitted with new leather clacks, a process known as 'grathing' or 'graving', or it was otherwise repaired. To get the bucket in position opposite the bucket door to facilitate its removal the spear rods were brought to rest on chock pieces of suitable length placed between the banging beam offset and the banging beams.

In the Cornish system the spear rods were of a size and weight sufficient to push the rams down in the ram chamber on the down stroke and thus force the water up the rising column. The main job of the single acting engine, where the steam acted only on the top side of the piston, was to lift the rods, rams and the bottom buckets. Sometimes both buckets and rams were made of iron but at Blundells' colliery, where the water was very corrosive, they were made of brass. It will be seen that in the case of the Cornish engine, the large section rods (at Blundells' they were of pitch pine 14in square in section and 56ft to 60ft long, Fig 23) were open to the shaft and required at intervals either two buntons with cross members to form a square known as 'collaring', through which the spear rod worked or, as at the Pemberton Engine Pit, 9in square buntons at 10yd intervals, on alternate sides of the spear rods. These buntons were fitted with cast iron brackets bolted to them and between which the rod worked. Where the spear rod worked through the guides, hardwood cleats, or (again as at Pemberton) wrought iron plates slightly longer than the stroke of the pumps were fitted with countersunk bolts to the rods. These latter were known as rubbing plates and made a great clattering noise when the engine was in motion.

In the case of the Newcomen engines working bucket lifts only, the rods did not need to be as heavy as those of Cornish engines working mainly rams. For instance for an 8in bucket with a lift

23 A reconstruction of changing a broken pump rod at Blundells' Pemberton
    Colliery in 1915 *(J. Parkinson)*

of about 30 fathoms, rods 4in square were used, 6in square rods were used for a 12in bucket, 8in square rods for a 16in bucket and 10in square rods for a 22in bucket.

Towards the end of the eighteenth century, heavy cast iron pipes came into general use. These were generally 9ft in length with bracketed flanges and two bands at intervals of 3ft. The flanges had six to eighteen square holes in them, depending on the diameter of the pipe. Generally in the nineteenth century, the pipes were faced with just sufficient spigot to keep a ring in position. The joint rings were generally of iron wrapped in tarred flannel and they were caulked with iron filings and sal-ammoniac, but sometimes lead rings were used. Cast iron pipe ranges were generally supported in the pit shaft by collars, in a similar manner to elm pipes in order to keep the columns steady and prevent straining of the joints. A collar consisted of a bunton fixed horizontally across the shaft in front of the pipes and two smaller pieces of timber known as pudlocks placed at right angles to the bunton, one on each side of the pipe under the flange. The pudlocks were scooped out to fit the pipe accurately, each being let into the shaft side at one end and bolted to the bunton at the other. These collars were generally formed at each alternate pipe. Sometimes in small diameter shafts, as at Blundells' Pemberton Engine Pit, the buntons were fixed between the pipes and the shaft sides, the pipes being secured to the buntons by wrought iron clamps and bolts (Fig 24). In the case of both ram and bucket pumps, the suction pipe, known as the wind bore, or bottom piece, had a number of holes in the bottom part of it which were covered by the water in the sump of the shaft or cistern in which it was placed. These holes were made of such a size as to prevent pieces of wood or other debris from entering the wind bore with the water. Next above this was the clack piece which was provided with a door and contained the clack valve. This clack could be taken out for repair through the clack door and if there was a risk of this being impracticable it was made with a bow on the top so that a hook, called a fish piece, could be attached to the spear rods in place of the bucket, passed down the column and secured to the bow of the clack, which was thus lifted out of its seat and up the column of pipes.

Above the clack piece was the working barrel in which the bucket reciprocated. This was slightly bell-mouthed at each end and of a slightly less diameter than the pipe column so that the bucket could be drawn up easily for repairs or replacement in an emergency. Attached to the bucket were the spear rods extending upwards inside the column of pumps or pipes to the beam of the

24 A reconstruction of repacking the gland of the ram pump at Blundells'
Pemberton Colliery in 1915 (*J. Parkinson*)

engine, or to a 'set off' (or offset as it was known at Pemberton) attached to the main spear rods working other sets of pumps in the same pit shaft.

At the top of the working barrel was the bucket door piece, by removing the door of which the bucket could be taken out for repairs. As the rod descended the bucket moved down the working barrel, the clack below closed and prevented the water descending again to the wind bore and at the same time the bucket valves were opened and the water, except that displaced by the bucket and rod, remained in the working barrel. On the upstroke of the engine the bucket valves closed and the water which stood in the working barrel at the down stroke was lifted on top of the bucket up the pipes, whilst, owing to the pressure of the atmosphere on the water in the sump, it followed the bucket in its ascent and filled the working barrel. Care had to be taken in working the engine that the wind bore was covered by a foot or two of water otherwise air would be drawn in and this could put the engine off its stroke.

In the case of Hustler's Cornish pumping engine there were the necessary two clack pieces with their clacks and doors in the plunger or ram set of pumps one above and one below the pipe connection to the ram chamber. As the ram descended the bottom clack closed, the water passing through the upper clack to the column of pipes above. As the ram ascended the bottom clack opened and the water from the cistern followed its course. The water in the column of pipes, by its weight, closed the upper clack.

We have fragmentary descriptions of three Orrell beam pumping engines and their associated pit work. The Old Engine of 1792 and the New Engine at Clarke's Winstanley Colliery (Fig 25) were almost certainly of the improved Newcomen Type, but the new one — if it was built by Robert Daglish after he took over the management of Haigh Foundry — may have been a great improvement on the 'common fire engine', those built by Daglish being 'celebrated in their day as improved and efficient machines'. Clarke's engine pit was 76yd to the Orrell Four Feet Seam and we may assume it was at least 80yd to the sump.

William Barton of Winstanley, formerly pump-man at Clarke's colliery in Winstanley, stated in 1875 that when the colliery was working they had a good deal of water and there were two pumping engines. Both of these lifted the water in two lifts, cisterns being fixed half way up the shaft. In the case of the Old Engine of 1792, the bottom lift bucket was 12½in diameter and the stroke 7ft and the lift from the cistern to the top of the pit was 12¼in

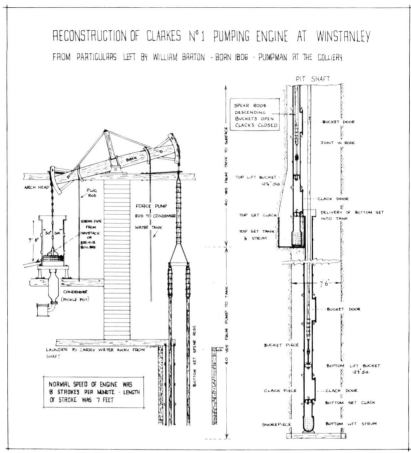

25 Clarke's No 1 pumping engine, built in 1792. Based on details left by
William Barton the colliery pumpman

diameter with the same stroke. The engine worked eight strokes
a minute. The diameter of both bottom and top lifts of the New
Engine was 11½in the stroke being 6ft. It worked nine strokes a
minute. Normally these engines worked 20 to 22 hours a day, but
after an inrush when they inadvertently holed through to old water-
logged workings, the engines worked night and day for between
two and three years, before they got rid of the 'dead' water. The
Old Engine cylinder would need to be about 50in diameter to lift
a column of water 240ft high in pipes 12½in diameter, allowing

for a working pressure on the piston of 8lb/in^2 and it would deliver about 265 gallons per minute allowing for slip etc. The New Engine which was slightly smaller, but worked at a higher speed, had a cylinder about 45in diameter and the pumps delivered approximately 215 gallons a minute, again allowing for slip.

At Blundells' Chain Colliery Engine Pit (Fig 20) the only particulars we have are the depth of the shaft, the height of the water column to the water tunnels to which the pump delivered and the daily 'make' of water which was 288,000 gallons. An atmospheric engine capable of raising 288,000 gallons per day 76yd 2ft to the borehole tunnels in 16 hours would be quite a large one, probably with a cylinder of about 40in diameter. There would be about 50yd of dry rods between the tunnels and the engine beam. There being two separate tunnels and boreholes, it is possible that two sets of rods, buckets and pump stocks were worked from the beam unless, as at Clarke's Engine Pit and later at Blundells' Pemberton Engine Pit, there were two engines.

In all probability the largest pumping engine in Orrell would be the one Blundells erected to drain their colliery on Catteralls estate near Kitt Green as it was in that area that the Orrell Four Feet Seam lay at its deepest.

The last of the Orrell pumping engines was erected in 1846 by John Mildred Hustler at his new Orrell Colliery, but it is quite possible that it was brought from one of their other pits that had by that time become exhausted. It was described as a 'Cornish Beam Condensing Pumping Engine' having a 59in diameter piston with a 7ft stroke. It had a beam in halves weighing 12 tons and it was fitted with Cornish valves and a cateract motion. The piston rod was 14ft long and 4½in diameter. The engine house was built of stone 22ft wide by 29ft long and three storeys high, the roof being covered with grey slate (flagstone). The engine worked four sets of pumps, the top one 71yd below the surface being a ram, pumping from a cistern through 15in stocks or pipes. Below this a 15in bucket lifted the water 87yd through 15in pipes to the ram cistern and 18yd below this in the shaft sump there were two other bucket lifts, one 12in diameter and the other 9in. In the engine house there was a treble-purchase crab with a wrought-iron frame which was used for lifting off the cylinder cover etc. A pair of shear legs 46ft 8in high stood over the shaft and these were used in conjunction with a powerful treble-purchase crab fitted with a brake ring bolted to a massive pitch-pine frame. The drum of the crab contained a long length of flexible steel rope. The height of the shear legs would seem to indicate the spear rods at this pit were not more than 40ft in length.

G

The job of a pitman or shaftman in these engine pits was an unenviable one. The shafts were mostly very cold and wet, similar to the one at Blundells' Pemberton Colliery which, sunk in the period 1815-20, was unlined except near the surface. The water poured down the shaft and in winter it was bitterly cold. The shaft men were provided annually with fustian suits which consisted of trousers, waistcoat and short jacket; they were also provided with a sleeveless leather jacket known at Pemberton as a 'backskin' and a sou'wester. A small hoppet made from half a barrel and fitted with wrought iron straps and four hangers was the only means of riding up and down the shaft (Fig 26), except when they rode escort on a bunton or pipe or some other heavy piece of equipment balancing the swaying load and clinging to the chains as it went down the shaft. The unsteady tub was used because there was so much equipment in the 9ft 6in diameter shaft with its massive pipe ranges and the supporting buntons, spear rods and offsets and their guides, that it was impossible to get a vertical run down and the tub had to be pushed from side to side in order to pass the obstructions and prevent the men from being tipped out. Open torches were used by the men and slung from the hoppet chains.

Sir William Fairbairn, the great engineer, gives us a vivid description of what it was like working in an engine pit in Northumberland in 1810 whilst he was serving his apprenticeship. The description is typical of the work in these engine pits:

> The duties were at times exceedingly severe and trying to the constitution, particularly in winter; and from the nature of the water which contained both salt and sand the wear and tear upon the pumps was very great. I however, designed every possible means to keep the pumps in good repair, but much depended upon the quality of the leather used for the buckets and clacks and as in some cases I have known a bucket wear to pieces in half an hour whilst others would last for a couple of days. The depth of the pit was 150 fathoms with four sets of pumps and what with broken pump rods and other casualties, I have frequently been suspended by a rope during the winter nights with the water pouring down upon me for seven to eight hours at a stretch, until every limb was numbed with cold. This often repeated, and being roused out of bed at all hours and having to descend the shaft (which was a cold downcast draught) — with flannel shirt and trousers, a leather hat and buckskin to protect the head and neck from the water which descended like a shower bath, the whole duty on these occasions was one of great severity in fact so severe as seriously to injure the health of one and destroy the life of another of my fellow assistants. These trials and many others of nearly equal severity I have with the blessing of God and a strong constitution, overcome, for which I have ever felt most grateful.

26 Reconstruction of repair men inspecting the pumping shaft at Blundells'
Pemberton Colliery in 1915. Note the pump pipes, with the pump rod
to the right *(J. Parkinson)*

Many accidents occurred in these pumping pits. The writer's father worked in Blundells' Engine Pit at various times during his apprenticeship and, just like Fairbairn, he had many stories to tell of accidents and miraculous escapes in the shaft. The writer himself remembers vividly, when a small schoolboy, gazing up one sunny autumn afternoon at the tall engine house at this pit on the day that three men had fallen down the shaft when a scaffold had collapsed; one had fallen 18ft and had managed to cling to a pipe flange, another had hit an obstruction and had ended up in a seam mouthing 45ft below where they were working. Both of these men were only shaken, but the third man fell 240ft to his death. His body was found tightly wedged between two ranges of pipes. He was the last of the many victims to be claimed locally during more than two centuries of engine pit working.

2.7 VENTILATION, LIGHTING AND EXPLOSIONS

In the early part of our period, when the shallow Orrell Five Feet Seam was being extensively worked, the workings were drained for the most part by soughs. The mouths of these soughs were of course much lower than the tops of the coal-drawing shafts and because of this, there was an alternating flow of air through the workings in the hot and cold seasons of the year. In the winter, the air would enter the sough and return up the shaft, but in summer it would travel in the opposite direction. Being very shallow, it is unlikely that much firedamp was encountered as most of this would have drained to the surface through the fissures or pores in the overlying rocks. This drainage of gas from shallow seams was the reason for the famous 'burning streams' or 'burning wells' of Hawkley and Hindley in the seventeenth century.

Ventilating the deeper Orrell Four Feet Seam however, would be a more difficult proposition. We have seen that mainly because of the underground transport system of dragging baskets on sledges to the pit shaft and the collier having contracted to do this, a great number of shafts were sunk to work a given area. This in itself would facilitate natural ventilation; for example Clarke's Winstanley Colliery where, following the normal practice, the coal was worked from the extreme dip side of the area to the rise, the difference between the surface level of the Engine Pit on the dip side and the furthermost pit on the rise was 150ft. The difference in the level of the seam at the two shafts was 325ft. The main water-road from this Engine Pit to the pits on the rise, which, under the terms of the lease had to be well maintained, would also act as the main airway. Shafts to be sunk especially for 'communicating air' are mentioned in the lease and these were probably furnace shafts. This method of ventilation was in use at Orrell during the first two decades of the nineteenth century, as two rectangular shafts 5ft square with their sides coated with soot were discovered fifty years ago on the site of Blundells' Chain Colliery. Various methods of ventilating mines had been tried out during the late seventeenth and eighteenth centuries. One was to lower an iron fire-bucket into a special air shaft, with a connection to the main upcast shaft a few yards from the surface, the top of the latter being covered by a door. The main point in this idea was to make the main shaft usable to some extent. Sometimes a furnace was placed at the bottom of a high chimney at the surface which was connected to the air shaft. A large furnace of this type at Laffak Colliery, Garswood, produced 17,500cu ft of air per minute in the middle of the last century. But this was a very old colliery and the system may have been in use for many years.

Some of the early pit bottom furnaces introduced into our district were not very successful. As late as the middle of the nineteenth century, the Winstanley No 1 Pit furnace circulated only 5,400cu ft of air per minute, and those at Blackleyhurst Seneley Green Pit and Little Delf Pit 8,652 and 4,763cu ft per minute respectively.

Although the Orrell Collieries finished in the middle of the nineteenth century, it may be of interest to see what was happening at the newer pits at that time or very shortly afterwards. By 1858, the furnace at Blundells' Venture Pit at Pemberton circulated 44,740cu ft per minute, that at the Bye Pit 40,340cu ft per minute and the one at the Tanpits 44,850cu ft per minute. All the brickwork of the furnaces in contact with the flames was of firebrick set in ground fireclay but this was generally backed up by ordinary brickwork, sometimes with a cavity of a few inches interposed between. In the gassy pits, it became necessary to use dumb drifts which were generally constructed at an inclination of not less than one in six and it was up these dumb drifts that the return air passed into the upcast shaft without going over the furnace, thus avoiding as far as possible, the danger of igniting the firedamp.

In order to avoid the danger associated with furnaces, various other means were sought to provide good ventilation, the first practical proposition was the use of high pressure steam jets at the bottom of the shaft provided with steam by underground boilers.

During the 1860s fan ventilation was introduced, an excellent example of this being the Guibal Fan at the King Pit at Blundells'

Pemberton Colliery. This was probably the largest fan in the country being 46ft in diameter and 14ft 10in wide, driven by a 36in cylinder engine erected in 1872. It ran at 48rpm and produced 314,000cu ft per minute at a water gauge of 2.8in.

The miner frequently refers to the noxious mine atmospheres and gases as various kinds of 'damps' from the German word 'dampf' meaning vapour, fog or fumes. The two most common of these met within coal mines are blackdamp and firedamp. The former is a mixture of the extinctive gases carbon dioxide and excess nitrogen. It is also sometimes referred to as choke damp or stythe in other coalfields. Firedamp is synonymous with methane or a mixture of gases, chiefly inflammable, given off naturally from coal and consisting for the most part of methane. Both the Orrell seams are gassy at depth, a large quantity of firedamp being recorded in the Orrell Four Feet Seam in 1860 at Blundells' Tanpits at Pemberton Colliery, but the depth there was 250yd. Indeed an enormous outburst of gas occurred in the Orrell Four Feet, or Arley Seam as it is known there, at Kirkless Hall Colliery, in 1859. Mr Higson the Inspector of Mines at the time who must have known the Orrell Collieries well, when asked if the Arley Seam was remarkable for firedamp, replied that 'this seam under whichever name it is known throughout its whole extent, gives off firedamp'.

However, the inspector's report on the explosion which occurred at the Winstanley New Colliery in 1860 stated that little gas was found in the workings there mainly because they were worked at a very slow rate. This colliery had been worked since the 1830s and it was working the Orrell Five Feet and Four Feet Seams 1,000yd distant from Clarke's workings. The furnace produced 10,225cu ft of air per minute, 5,300cu ft of which passed directly to the furnace, but leakages through brattices in addition to this reduced the amount of air going round the workings, to 4,102cu ft per minute. No air stoppings were of brick but were constructed of cloth. Although Davy lamps were used in the extraction of the pillars, candles were used in the straits or narrow places. It was difficult at some collieries to induce the men to use safety lamps; they much preferred candles because of the better light and indeed they became experts at testing for gas with a candle. Joseph Dickinson, the first Inspector of Mines for Lancashire, Cheshire, North Wales, Staffordshire, Shropshire and Warwickshire, had been a pupil in the 1830s of Thomas Sopwith of Newcastle upon Tyne. Sopwith had been brought up by the famous John Buddle. Dickinson had this to say about trying for gas 'with a candle'. The presence of inflammable gas, from the slightest mixture, through all its gradations to the firing point, was readily discovered by an experienced collier, and he judged very correctly of the degree of inflammability and danger which threatened the safety of the mine by attentively observing the appearance of the spire or cap upon the top of the candle. The common pit candles varied in size, but those generally used were 45 to the lb; the wick was of cotton and the candle made of ox or sheep tallow; but clean ox tallow was best.

The mode of trying the candle, as it was called, to ascertain the mixture of inflammable gas, was as follows:

In the first place, the candle called by the colliers the low was trimmed, that is, the liquid fat was wiped off, the wick snuffed short, and carefully cleaned of red embers, so that the flame might burn as purely as possible. The candle being thus prepared, it was holden between the fingers and thumb of the one hand and the palm of the other was placed between the eye of the observer and the flame, so that nothing but the spire of, the flame could be seen as it gradually towered over the upper margin of the hand. The observation was generally commenced near the floor of the mine and the light and hand were gently raised upwards, till the true state of the circulating current could be ascertained. The first indication of the circulation of inflammable air was a slight tinge of blue or a bluish grey colour shooting up from the top of the spire of the candle, and terminating in a fine extended point. This spire increased in size and received a deeper tinge of blue as it rose through an increased proportion of inflammable gas, till it reached the firing point; but the experienced collier knew accurately enough all the gradations of show (as it was called) upon the candle and was very rarely fired upon, excepting in cases of sudden discharges of inflammable gas.

Carlyle Spedding, the manager of the Lowther Collieries at Whitehaven had introduced the flint and steel mill in the middle of the eighteenth century. This consisted of a geared steel disc worked by a handle and set in a light frame. The steel disc revolved against a piece of flint and produced a shower of sparks which gave a feeble light but enabled the collier to carry on his work in the presence of gas. A boy was required to work the mill. Dickinson said that although inflammable air had frequently fired at the sparks of steel mills, it only happened (from all the facts Mr Buddle had been able to collect) when the mills were played near the place where the gas was discharged. Dickinson had seen them in use in dangerous states of air but he believed 'that the change of appearance of the sparks, if attentively observed gave sufficient notice of the threatening danger'. Underground firemen, or deputies as they are now known since terms became standardised, derived their name from the very dangerous performance they had to carry out daily underground. In speaking of the collieries of this district Dickinson said that he found that:

in some mines with sluggish ventilation, it was customary to burn fire-damp in places in advance of the air. This, as I have watched it, was done by lighting the extreme tail of the gas, which sent flames hissing along to the face about as quickly as a person could walk.

As the flame passed, it lighted the feeders of gas and left them burning with blue flames, which had to be flapped out. This was in fiery mines but, of course, where there was not sufficient air to make the mixture explosive. It was called burning out the firedamp. If air became sucked in sufficient to cause an explosion, it was said to have burst.

This was practised where powder was used for blasting, the burning and flapping out had to be done before firing a shot, and the flapping out had to be repeated after the shot had relighted the feeders.

When the old Holland Colliery at Crawford, UpHolland, holed through into old workings many years ago, the main road was found to contain specially-made cavities in the roof where the gas could collect and be fired by the fireman before the beginning of the working shift.

Blackdamp perhaps gave the Orrell proprietors more trouble than firedamp and this is generally the case with workings that are not very deep. Blackdamp is heavier than air, lies on the floor of the mine and gives warning of its presence by the extinction of the candles or lamps and, coupled with its effect in deepening the breathing, generally gives time for the miner to withdraw. It is found in old unventilated goaves or sinks and has been found by the writer on two occasions when boring to back-filled opencast workings. One of these samples was particularly lethal as there was less than 2 per cent of oxygen in the mixture. Another example of the fatal effects of blackdamp was seen when we sank a shaft into some old abandoned workings. During the working shift, the shaft was ventilated by a fan, but when the men went to work in the morning, they often found dead birds which had roosted on the timber lining only 6in below the top of the shaft indicating that the blackdamp was spilling out of the workings.

The fireman, who sixty years ago was in charge of the No 3 East District in the Wigan Nine Feet Seam at Blundells' Pember-ton Colliery, told how the blackdamp came out of the goaf into the working places almost as fast as a man could walk when there was a sudden drop in the barometric pressure. He got into the habit of holding his lamp at chest height because if he lowered it, below his chest, it would often be extinguished by the black-damp.

Enough has been said to show the serious difficulties they would encounter in working the deeper Orrell Four Feet Seam at Orrell with the inadequate ventilation and unsafe lights of those days.

Another gas was the dreaded 'afterdamp' resulting from an explosion of firedamp and containing carbon monoxide. This accounted for many deaths of those who had survived death and maiming from the actual violence of an explosion.

2.8 COAL PREPARATION, COKE BURNING AND MARKETS

Although some of the coal owners in the North-East Coalfield had introduced screening in the second half of the eighteenth century, the practice in Lancashire seems to have been the riddling of the coal at the coal face by the collier until well into the nineteenth century. In fact it is very doubtful if any other system existed during the working life of the main Orrell collieries.

Riddles of ¾in and 1in mesh were in use and the slack, surplus to requirements for coke burning and sales, was stowed underground. However, there was a limited market for slack, which increased very considerably between 1794 and 1800 at Blundells' Orrell Colliery. During 1788 for example, sales of house coal brought in £9,737 9s 11d (£9,737.50) and 'sleck' £7 17s 10d (£7.89), but in 1800 sales of house coal had almost trebled to £27,308 5s 3d (£27,308.26) whilst sales of slack had increased 140 times to £1,111 11s 3d (£1,111.56). This would most likely be Orrell Five Feet slack which had a high calorific value.

During the early days of our period after the opening of the Douglas Navigation, many of the new customers were in the Fylde district and some as far afield as Kendal and Milnthorpe, but some of the coal was sent along the coast to Liverpool from the mouth of the Douglas. After the opening of the Leeds and Liverpool canal, when the large collieries had been established, most of the coal went down the canal to Liverpool. Indeed, a number of the leases insisted that none of the coal produced should be sold locally. Offices were established near the basin of the canal in Liverpool, Blundells' being at 1 Leeds Street; the office of Hustler and Hardcastle was close by. In fact during the next hundred years most of the coal firms' offices, including Bankes and Woodcock & Haliburton, were situated in Old Hall Street which adjoins Leeds Street. Lord Balcarres's office was at 68 Old Hall Street.

In 1766 the coal bought on trust at the Lower Coal Pits at Winstanley was sold to customers at Pemberton, Winstanley, Orrell, UpHolland and Ormskirk, the proportion being approximately 57, 16, 11, 8, and 8 per cent respectively. During the same year, the sales from the Upper Coal Works near the Orrell to Ashton road were in the following proportions: Liverpool 26 per cent, Billinge

25 per cent, Warrington 16 per cent, Winstanley 9 per cent, Ashton 8 per cent, Prescot 5 per cent, Ditton & Windle 4 per cent, Ormskirk 3 per cent, Wigan 2 per cent, UpHolland 2 per cent.

An account book, showing discounts on coal sales given by Blundells and also bad debts between 1788 and 1800, discloses that the customers were mostly merchants indicated by familiar names such as Thomas and William Earle, celebrated Liverpool merchants; William Gregson, Africa merchant and banker; John Blackburne, an important figure in the salt trade; J & C Shaw, bottle manufacturers; Wakefield and Oakhill, salt boilers; Ewart & Ritson, Africa merchants; John Sparling, export merchant and slave trader, much of whose exports consisted of textiles; Roe & Co, brass founders, who supplied copper and brass goods to merchants in the African slave trade. Other familiar names were Lofthouse and Co coal merchants, Skelhorne and Co, Luke Babe one time customs jerquer, Robert Norris, William Leece and many others.

Besides these there were public institutions such as the Liverpool Infirmary, the Bluecoat Hospital and the Corporation of Liverpool and sea captains like Collinson, Durack, Dixon, Holmes, Vessey and Parker to name only a few.

The prices of the Orrell coals were:

1.9d per cwt at Winstanley in 1747;
2.25d per basket (140lb) at Winstanley in 1754;
2.00d per basket at Winstanley in 1766;
2.30d per basket (140lb) at Orrell in 1773.

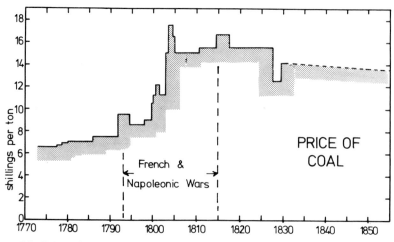

27 Price of Orrell coal delivered at Liverpool, 1773-1855

In November 1776, a ton of Orrell coal delivered at Wigan cost 7s (35p) and 9 baskets of Holmes Colliery coal 3s (15p) or 4d per basket. The pit head price at Jackson's Orrell House Colliery was 3s 2d per ton in 1754 and this price was paid by James Spencer 16 years later for 1 ton delivered to Dean Brook.

In 1785, the pit-head price at Orrell was 3d per basket of 140lb and in 1792 it had risen to 4d for a basket of 150lb. The delivered price of the Orrell coals in Liverpool varied as shown in Fig 27.

From the onset of the war in 1793 the rising price of coal followed the increase in prices of most other commodities. During the 25 years following 1831 there was little change in the price of coal, as in 1857 Blundells were offering the best Orrell coal from their Pemberton Colliery at 13s 6d (67½p) per ton delivered by boat alongside in the Nelson Dock or by wagon alongside at Garston Docks.

Blundells, together with the other Orrell colliery owners, had a very large trade with Ireland, and indeed exported coal to the United States and to South America. Blundells retained these Irish customers until World War II, although after the Orrell Four Feet and Five Feet Seams became exhausted at Pemberton in the mid-twenties of the present century, it became increasingly difficult to retain them. For well over a century they had been supplied with these famous coals and it was hard for them to accept second best.

The Orrell Four and Five Feet Seams, especially the former, made the finest coke and soon after the Douglas Navigation was opened, we find references to coal, charcoal and cinders (meaning coke). Coke could be made in heaps or mounds in the open air, a portion of the heap being allowed to burn away completely to supply the necessary heat. The low yield of coke, however, made the open mound process inefficient and attempts were made to improve the process by confining the coal inside beehive-shaped ovens, 10-11ft diameter and 6-7ft high. Sometimes, however, these ovens were rectangular in plan. The necessary air for combustion was controlled by means of dampers and flues. In the enclosed beehive-type of oven, the volatile matter hitherto completely wasted was burnt inside the chamber supplying a great portion of the heat, formerly obtained at the expense of the coke itself.

That coke ovens were in use at Orrell in the second half of the eighteenth century is evident from the records. On 4 March 1777 Hustler and Hardcastle paid Holt Leigh 'for bricks for an oven', and 'Oven coke' was frequently mentioned in local colliery accounts during this period. Later in June 1817, Meyrick Bankes paid £1 for carting slack to his oven at Orrell and as early as March

1766 William Bankes paid 3s (15p) for burning 100 baskets of 'cinders' at his Winstanley pits. Blundells' account book which begins in 1788 records sales of 'coal charcoal' every year up to 1797. The early ovens were either built singly or in batteries of two to four and in the later ones the flues connected them to a chimney, the connection of each oven to this flue being controlled by a damper. To make coke, a charge of slack was put into the oven and a red hot piece of iron inserted in it to start the action, although the heat retained in the oven brickwork was generally sufficient to get it going. The charge was levelled off and the doorway bricked up. For a few hours the gas came off slowly but was not of a quality to ignite, but after a while, the gas came more freely and at this stage a little air was admitted above the charge to burn the gas, the heat from this combustion being reflected from the roof on to the charge below. The heat from the oven gradually increased and the whole of the volatile matter was finally expelled. This required about three days, and during the last stage of the coking, the door was thoroughly daubed with a mixture of clay and ground ash to exclude air entirely in order to avoid undue loss of coke. When all traces of gas was absent, the mass of incandescent coke was quenched inside the oven and the charge was then raked out.

2.9 SURFACE TRANSPORT

Probably the earliest colliery wagon roads or railways constructed in the Orrell area were those connecting Jackson's Orrell House Colliery and the Ayrefield Colliery with the Douglas Navigation at Gathurst. The Leeds and Liverpool canal had been completed as far as Dean Locks on the Lancashire side in 1774, but the Douglas was used to connect the canal with Wigan until the extension to Wigan, authorised in April 1776, was completed. It was on 1 November 1776 that an advertisement appeared in the *Liverpool General Advertiser:*

> Messrs Warren & Co. [Warren, Blundell, Earle and Chaffers] beg leave to acquaint the PUBLIC THAT they have completed a waggon road from Mr Jackson's Coal Mines in Orrell (near Wigan) down to the Canal by which Coal is brought down to their Yard in Liverpool, without being subject to so much breakage, as those from other Mines upon the said Canal.

When the Gathurst to Wigan stretch of the canal was completed, it became necessary to extend the two wagon roads and carry them over the Douglas by means of bridges to connect them with the canal. The Liverpool Committee of the Leeds and Liverpool Canal Co recommended that the wagon ways be

> continued across the Douglas from the Collieries so as Boats may lie and be loaded in the canal. Resolved that it is the opinion of this Committee that the Company of Proprietors of the Canal, ought to be at the Expense of making, or continuing, the Waggon Roads from Mr Jackson's Colliery and also one from the Ayrefield Colliery, over the River Douglas to the Canal, in Consideration of the expense which the Owner or workers, of these collieries, have been at in making their present Conveniences for loading; but that the proprietors of the canal should not afterwards keep them in repair.

In October 1775, James Corless and James Marsh made a valuation of 'Timber, Trees and plants now growing in Orrell Brow to be removed (by Mr Longbothom) in order to complete the Waggon road'. Thirty-five trees 'fit for rails or pilos' were mentioned in the accounts. 'Pilo' or pillow may have been another name for sleeper. It is very likely that this refers to the Ayrefield Colliery railway as Longbothom was a partner in it.

At that time both the rails and the sleepers were of wood as is evident from an advertisement concerning Berry's Orrell Post House Colliery dated 23 April 1781 which describes the wagon road there as 'a good and commodious Railed or Plank Road that coals may be got down at an easy expense to the Leeds Canal; the road made of new Oak Timber'. Berry had only constructed his wagon road during the previous twelve months, as in 1789 he had been granted permission to build it on condition that

> he make a Strong Rampart Bank ten yards long against the Bank of the Canal towards the river of equal Height at least with the Bank of the Canal and that the rest of the railed road between the said Canal and the old river be supported on Pillars and that in the Execution of such work he do not Stop the Navigation above Seven Days.

This bank, it would seem, was to facilitate the unloading of wagons into flats.

These wooden tracks varied in detail from place to place, but they were usually constructed of sleepers, about 5-6ft in length and 6-8in square. Sometimes they were left in the round except for the ends on which the rails fitted, which were squared with an adze. The sleepers were set about 15in to 3ft apart and the rails themselves were of oak, ash or beech and generally about 4½in wide by 5in high. They were pegged to the sleepers by oak pegs or tree nails hammered in holes bored through the rail and part way through the sleepers. The track was ballasted with slack, coke breeze or any other handy material. Indeed Blundells' early nineteenth century railway to their Venture Pits at Pemberton and the sidings connected with them were ballasted with hundreds of tons of unsaleable coke breeze. In recent years, coal recovery firms have made profits by selling good quality slack ballast from old colliery tracks in the Wigan area.

Heavy wear on the rails induced the colliery owners to adopt the double rail system. This consisted of simply pinning an easily replacable second rail on top of the bottom one. The ballast could also be filled in to a higher level over the top of the sleepers and this protected them from the horses hooves. A further development was the laying of wrought or cast iron strips along the top of the wooden rails. This not only prevented the wooden rails from wearing but also diminished the friction. However, trouble was experienced with the nails constantly working loose and the plates were used mostly on curves and inclines in order to lessen the load on the horses.

The rolling stock of the wagon road from Orrell House Colliery in 1780 consisted of thirteen wagons. There were twenty-eight horses at the colliery, at that time, but how many were wagon-road horses and how many were gin horses, it is not possible to say. In addition to the thirteen coal wagons there was a lime wagon, three 6in wheel carts, one wagon with broad and narrow wheels and a 'weigh engine'.

Before the end of the eighteenth century there were four main lines and many branch lines to the various pits. As each pit had a very short working life, it was necessary to be constantly engaged on laying new branches to the pits being sunk and taking up track that had served worked-out pits. During this century the sidings were still referred to as 'branches' in the cost-sheets of Blundells' Pemberton Colliery. (See Fig 12, page 53).

It was because of the necessity to sink numerous pits and lay wagon roads to them that the whole of the surface of an estate had to be taken in lease along with the minerals. Colliery owners were not always free to use their railways as they pleased, royalty owners sometimes objecting to coal from other estates passing over lines on theirs. On the 9 March 1789, Henry Blundell sent the following letter to Holt Leigh:

> Having bought some coals from Mr Holme which it was our intention to have brought through our estate by the means of Hustler and Co's Waggon Road, but we understand by our Agent that you have forbid it. We mean to be at Wigan tomorrow at 11 o'clock if it is agreeable to you and shall be glad to meet you at the Eagle and Child at that time.

After 1791 both Blundell and Hustler worked Holt Leigh's coal and there was an agreement that they could lay wagon roads over each other's lands if they found it necessary or convenient. Blundell wrote to Holt Leigh 18 June 1798:

> I have perused the Agreement for the accommodation of wagon roads between Messrs Hustler & Co and ourselves over the lands of each other for the purpose of conveying the coals of each to the River Douglas and Leeds canal and find that we have full power of making Roads over all the lands in lease to Messrs Hustler and Co.

Blundell had taken a lease of the Duke of Bridgewater's coal in Winstanley under what is now known as Duke's Barn Farm and he was busy laying a wagon road to it which was an extension of the one he had taken over Holt Leigh's land. Holt Leigh objected to Blundell bringing Bridgewater coal over his land but Blundell said

> there is no exception made in the agreement as to the bringing of any person's Coals upon the wagon roads. I trust and intreat Sir, you will not put us to any inconvenience to carry our Coals from the Estate of the Duke of Bridgewater, for they are no longer *his* but our coals.

£10 per acre was the rent payable by Blundell to Hustler for a wagon road constructed over Hustler's land and vice versa.

Before the end of the eighteenth century iron rails both wrought or cast-iron edge rails and cast-iron plate rails had been introduced together with stone sleepers. Holt, in his *Agriculture of Lancashire* published in 1796, gives a drawing of a light plateway and Blundells' wagon way from the Orrell House and Chain Collieries near Dean Wood may have been converted from a wooden road to a plate road as many rails of this pattern were found in a shaft-filling on the Chain Colliery site in the 1920s. These were described by Mr Ernest Holland of Orrell as being 3ft in length, the base 4in broad, the flange 3in high and the thickness ½in or slightly more. There were three spike holes in the plates for fixing them to the sleepers (Fig 28).

Important developments were soon to take place, which gave Orrell the distinction of being the site of the operation of one of the world's earliest successful locomotives. It has been mentioned in the section describing Clarke's Collieries that Robert Daglish became the manager there, probably about 1810. In 1812 he converted the old wagonway to iron rails and stone sleepers with a view to running a rack locomotive of Blenkinsop's design on it. Blenkinsop's locomotive, which he had built in 1812, was fitted with a toothed driving wheel between the wheels on the left-hand side of the engine which engaged with specially-cast cogged rails. Later engines had these toothed driving wheels on both sides to reduce side pull. The cogs on the rails were formed by semi-circular

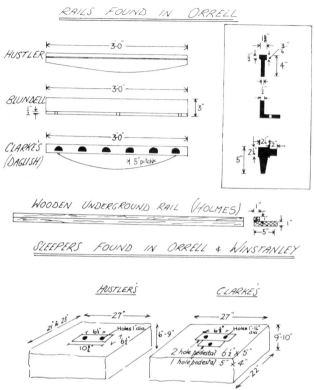

28 *(above)* Cast iron and wooden rails found at Orrell. *(below)* Stone sleeper-blocks found at Orrell and Winstanley. The pedestal hole centres seem to be a standard 6½in

extensions cast on the sides of the edge rails and of symetrical shape; the pitch between each cog was 6in. The gauge of this railway was 4ft. Many of the stone sleepers are still to be seen along the old track, now used as a farm road and public footpath and known locally as Nicholsons Lane, although it is shown on the OS maps as Hall Lane. One of these Daglish sleepers reposes in the writer's garden, its dimensions are 27in wide on the sides at right angles to the track by 22in on the sides parallel to the track. It is between 9in and 10in thick and has three holes drilled right through it and weighs about 200lb. Nearly all the surviving blocks on the Peak Forest tramway have three peg holes, the earlier single peg stone blocks having been converted to take two peg saddles. It can clearly be seen in the case of the writer's sleeper that there was a chair or saddle 7in by 4in spiked down to the single peg, the hole for which was 1¼in diameter. After its conversion, a chair 8in by 5in was spiked to two plugs which were 1in diameter and set at

6½in measured diagonally across the chair (Fig 28). On the other hand since the holes went right through the sleeper, these latter chairs may not have been spiked, as Daglish introduced the method of bolting them down to the sleeper. Years afterwards he won a prize from the London and Birmingham Railway Co for the best design of a chair. He is also said to have introduced fishplates. Stone sleepers on the wagon line from Bankes's new colliery at Winstanley to the Wigan Pier Head on the Leeds and Liverpool canal were 20in square and 9in thick with two 1in diameter holes set 6½in apart. Similar sleepers can still be seen on the site of Blundells' Tanpits at Pemberton. In Blundells' wages book for 1827 there are many payments for the drilling of stone sleepers and for 'laying new road' ie a wagon road.

An early nineteenth century plan shows the main line of Clarke's wagon way as a double road all the way from Winstanley to Crooke. It ran from Winstanley across a stone viaduct known locally as 'The Arches' over the valley at the Pingot near to the present bridge over the Wigan to Liverpool main line, and from there it ran to a

29 Clarke's wagon road at Winstanley, showing the stone sleeper-blocks. On here ran Daglish's *Yorkshire Horse*, Lancashire's first steam locomotive

30 The line of Clarke's wagon road at Kitt Green

point near the junction of Bradshaw Street and Ormskirk Road, [*orrell*]
a place formerly known as 'The Gossips'. From there it ran in a
straight line to a point near Bell House Farm, where it followed
Prescott Lane, turned off at Eccles Road and went past the Baiting Houses and on to the pier head on the canal a quarter of a
mile west of Crooke Hall. The eventual total length of Clarke's
wagon road was 3½ miles and the fall to the canal at Crooke was
205 ft.

Horse fodder had become extremely dear by 1811 and some
colliery owners began to show interest in the newly-invented steam
locomotive as an alternative to horse traction. The earliest locos
had been too heavy for the track and destroyed it, so track was
strengthened and attempts were made to cut down on the weight
of new locomotives.

In 1812, by arrangement with Blenkinsop, Robert Daglish constructed a locomotive to the patentees' specification at Haigh Foundry, Wigan (Fig 34). This locomotive was put to work in January
1813 and was famous locally as *The Yorkshire Horse*. Benjamin
Hick of the Union Foundry, Bolton, whose name is perpetuated
in the well-known firm of Bolton engineers — Hick Hargreaves,
gave a good description of Daglish's locomotives and the work they
performed in a letter he wrote to *The Kaleidoscope or Literary
and Scientific Mirror* for 1822. After commenting on the fact that

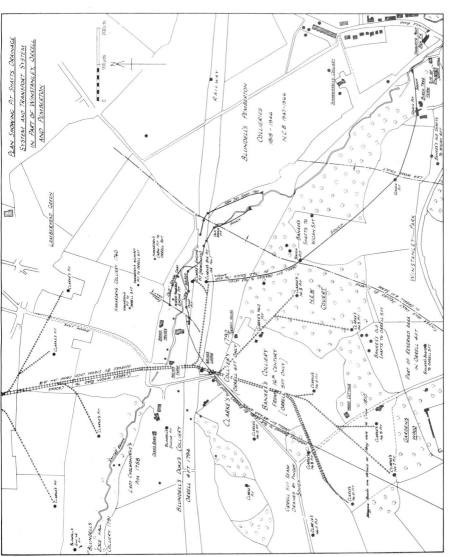

31 Plan of pits, drainage and transport south of Lamberhead Green

32 Viaduct known as 'The Arches' which carried Clarke's wagon road across the Pingot Valley. Demolished about 1890. *(Wigan Public Library)*

33 Daglish's cast-iron bridge, which replaced two arches of the Pingot Viaduct in 1848 when the main railway line was constructed through it. Removed to its present position at the turn of the century

Not the slightest accident has occurred during the whole time this mode of drawing coal waggons has been adopted at the Orrell Collieries near Wigan where there are three travelling steam engines,

he goes on to say that

two of these have been regularly at work for upwards of eight years; one of which is used to convey the coals up an incline railway half a mile in length and varying in ascent from 7/8 to 1 inch per yard. It draws at one time, 12 waggons of fully three tons each at the rate of 3 miles per hour besides its own weight, which when at work is 6½ tons, and would draw 90 tons at the same speed on a level road. Mr Daglish at the colliery states they occasionally run it at 4 to 5 miles per hour and that one engine performs the work which formerly required 14 horses.

When it arrives at the summit, the wagons are disengaged and it returns with the same number of empty ones previously brought by the other engine, which now takes them forward down a similar incline of about the same length, towards the canal, where the coals are put into vessels. These engines are on the high-pressure principle, requiring no water for condensation (the steam acting by its elasticity in proportion as it exceeds that of the atmosphere) and perform their work at three miles per hour when the pressure is equal to 32lbs per square inch. Each engine has two cylinders, 8 inches diameter with metallic pistons that require no packing, the rods of which are attached by crossbars and connecting rods to cranks placed at right angles with each other, to allow the full effect of the action of one of its greatest horizontal length of lever when the other is passing the top or bottom centre, where, of course, it can have no power in propelling the engine; no beam or fly wheel is used, the shafts on which the cranks are fastened have each a small pinion working into a spur wheel on another shaft passing under the engine framing on one end of which is a wheel with cogs of a coarse pitch working into the cogs on one side of the railway.

Daglish stated that these locos were in use for upwards of thirty-six years at the colliery and had made a saving of £500 per annum over the use of horses, drivers etc. Joseph Hilton, born in a public house at Orrell in 1849, had this to say when he was over 80 years old:

when Mr Daglish removed from Clarkes to Norley, he fixed up the engine part of the Yorkshire Horse in the colliery stables for hay cutting and mixing provender, with which I had much to do in my working days as colliery bricksetter in doing repairs about the stables and gas retorts. This relic which ought to have been more particularly noticed, passed away under the demolishers' hammer at the closing down of the collieries a few years ago [early 1920s].

Richard Eccles, master cotton spinner of Wigan, who had acquired the Walthew House Estate some years previously, had made an agreement in 1845 with Robert Daglish and his brother John for the lease of that portion of Clarke's wagon road which ran over his land. The term was 21 years and the rent £150 per annum.

34 A model of Blenkinsop's locomotive. The *Yorkshire Horse* was built to this
design at Haigh Foundry by Robert Daglish *(Science Museum)*

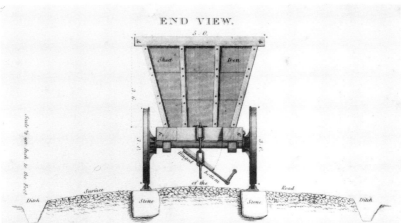

35 A coal waggon of about 1837, with a hinged bottom, also showing the construction of the wagon road. *(Science Museum)*

The lease was

> for the purpose of wagoning, carrying away and conveying over and above the same railway, coal, cannel or slack, the produce of a certain colliery in Winstanley of which he the said Robert Daglish is now the lessee, assignee, tenant or under tenant and the produce of certain coal mines thereto adjoining.

These seams adjoining belonged to Meyrick Bankes and may have been those under Winstanley Park, worked after 1856 from Blundells' Venture Pits. The Daglish's were also to have permission to take over the railway, coal, cannel and slack from pits sunk or to be sunk in the Norley Hall estate in Pemberton which belonged to John Daglish for which purpose they would have to construct a branch line. This branch came from Norley No 1 Pit near Kitt Green and joined Clarke's railway at the Baiting Houses. The line was worked by horses until the 1870s when it was converted to standard gauge and connected to the Lancashire and Yorkshire Railway. A stationary steam rope-haulage engine was erected at 'Orrell City' by Thomas Whaley the then owner of the colliery and for many years this was known as the *City Engine*.

Another important Orrell wagon road was that constructed by Hustler and Co, which after it had been extended in 1840 to their new Brownlow Colliery at Billinge Hill was four miles long and had an overall fall of 470ft to the canal at Gathurst. The portion that concerns us was completed before 1830, its terminus being at pits in the St James's Road area of Orrell. Not much is known about this line, but the route is shown on the 1849 OS sheet. Up to a few years ago, some of the embankments known to the local in- habitants as 'Ramfers' were to be seen in the fields between Abbey Lakes and Sefton Road and south-east of the Old Engine public house. The site of the inclined track down the ravine north of the Bird i'th Hand public house is clearly visible and the small arch under which the line passed on the east side of the railway bridge over the main road at the bottom of Gathurst Brow is still there, although the floor under the arch has been raised. The gauge is said to have been 3ft 6in. Judging by the width of the arch at Gathurst Bridge it could not have been much more than this and local tradition has it that Hustler's wagons were small ones. The rails were 3ft in length, and fish bellied and the stone sleepers were approximately 27in x 22in and 9in thick with 1in plug holes at 6½in centres. This was after its conversion from a wooden rail- way.

Joseph Hilton said he always understood that Woodcock and Haliburton carted their coal to Seven Stars Bridge at Wigan and, as nothing is known of any wagon roads from the pits of Jarratt and Lofthouse and Thomas Claughton, presumably they did like- wise, although they might have carted to some other point on the canal. The collieries of the Bankes family at Winstanley, and Holme at the south end of Dean Wood, supplied a more local sale and presumably a rail connection to the canal was not essential. How- ever, Clarke's wagon road ran through the site of the former coll- iery, and Blundells' Dean Wood wagon road with its extension to Dean Colliery ran close to Holme's pits, so it is possible they could be accommodated if they chose. An item in Holme's Colliery acc- ounts shows that the cart roads to the colliery were kept in order: '1799 By cash paid for paving a road to the Coal Pit £105. 4. 6.'

36 The main-line railway bridge at Gathurst. Hustler's wagon road ran under the small arch

37 Stone sleepers from Hustler's wagon road

CHAPTER THREE

Social Conditions

3.1 PERSONNEL, WAGES, CONDITIONS OF WORK AND DISPUTES

During the third quarter of the eighteenth century, the typical Orrell colliery consisted of a pumping engine pit, two or three whimsey or coal drawing pits and a shaft in process of being sunk. For example, in October 1771 Halliwell had two pits winding coal and one being sunk. The personnel consisted of the auditor, who, under Halliwell himself, managed the colliery, the engineman who worked the Newcomen-type pumping engine, the blacksmith who sharpened and tempered the collier's picks and wedges and made new ones besides making hammers and any other tools they required. There is no doubt also that together with the engineman, the blacksmith would have to attend to the day-to-day repairs and maintenance of the pumping engine with its boiler and the rods and bucket pumps in the shaft, as well as seeing to the whimseys at the coal drawing shafts.

There was a browman or banksman at each of the coal producing pits. They were responsible for taking the full baskets off the rope when they arrived at the pit brow and sending the empty ones down. They also had to see to the wheeling of the baskets to the heap or coal stack and this was generally done by youths or boys. Coal was despatched to the various customers or to the River Douglas by cart, although some of the local customers would cart their own. Three winders were employed, two at the coal winding pits and one at the sinking pit. They drove the gin or whimsey horses and no doubt had to attend to the feeding and grooming of the horses. They would also have to keep an eye on the condition of the harness, the ropes and shackles and the whimsey itself so that there would be as few stoppages as possible.

The winder at the sinking pit would also have to carry out the duties of browman, wheeling and tipping the baskets of dirt and levelling the dirt to form the new pit brow.

Two sinkers were employed at this time probably because there was, for some reason or other, no hurry in getting down to the coal. On other occasions when he was sinking a pit, Halliwell employed four men which would make better progress. In the two

working pits, there were eight colliers who employed seven drawers. Sometimes a basket maker or mender was employed, but Halliwell's accounts do not mention them.

A similar pattern emerges from the Winstanley Colliery accounts
for October 1766. There were five colliers employed in the Five
Feet Seam at the Moorhey Pit, four in the Lime Piece Pit, and at
that time one in the Salterley Pit. Three sinkers were engaged in
sinking a new pit.

The Orrell Colliery working the Orrell Five Feet belonging to the
Rev Thomas Holme (which, after his death in 1803, passed to his
son Meyrick, who had inherited the Winstanley Estate and changed
his name to Bankes) carried on in the same way until it closed in
1820. In 1782 seven colliers were employed and the number varied between four and five, until in 1790, there was a sudden increase to nine, dropping again to three in 1799, two in 1810 and
four in 1814.

However, this was unusual and the 'get-rich-quick' merchants
from Bradford and Liverpool had different ideas. In any case they
worked the deeper Four Foot Seam and needed a larger output
in order to get a return on their capital. To take the case of Hustler's and Blundells' collieries the progress is shown in Fig 38.

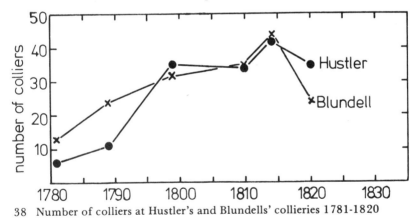

38   Number of colliers at Hustler's and Blundells' collieries 1781-1820

By the beginning of the nineteenth century, the methods of
working had progressed sufficiently to allow for the employment
of much larger numbers in each pit. The amount of capital outlay
necessary in sinking deeper pits, setting up expensive pumping engines and pumps and in some cases new steam winders, required
larger outputs and consequently more manpower to give a suitable return on the investment.

In 1766 at Winstanley, day wages varied from 8d (3½p) per day for a boy, 10d (4p) for a youth to 1s 1d (5½p), 1s 2d (6p), and 1s 4d (6½p) for men — those getting the highest rate probably being the best workmen. In 1798 Robert Holt Leigh paid 1s 10d (9p) per day for men and in 1817 at Meyrick Bankes's Orrell Colliery, the rates varied from 10d (4p) per day for a boy gin-driver, to 1s (5p) and 1s 2d (6p) for youths and 2s 2d (11p) for a man. Ten years later in 1827 at Blundells' collieries, 77 per cent of the men received 1s 8d (8½p) to 2s 2d (11p) per day while the maximum rate was 2s 8d (13½p) and the minimum only half of this. (Fig 39).

The rise in wages during the war years was, generally speaking, exceeded by the increase in the cost of living and so the miners were worse off, especially in the famine years of 1800-1 and 1810-12 when the cost of wheat rose to prodigious heights. However after 1815 the cost of living fell, but wages remained fairly stable, so that the miner had more to spend on drinking and gambling.

Typical wages for getting coal by the score in the early part of our period were 10d (4p) a score plus 1d for waydrawing paid at Winstanley Colliery in 1766 for getting, filling and drawing to the pit shaft, a score being twenty-four baskets, each weighing 140lb.

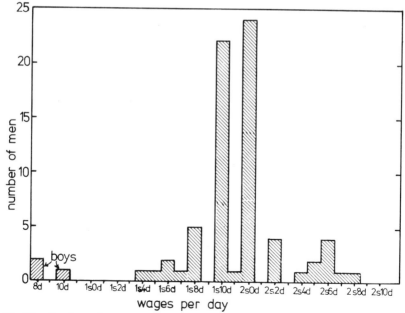

39 Distribution of wages for seventy-three men at Blundells' collieries in 1827

Halliwell paid 1s (5p) per score of 26 baskets of 150lb weight six years later. Longbothom in 1776 paid 1s (5p) for a similar score of baskets except that the baskets were of 140lb capacity. However, in 1817, Meyrick Bankes paid rates varying between 2s 2d (11p) and 2s 11d (14½p) for a similar score. This works out at 1s 5¼d (7p) to 1s 11¼d (9½p) per ton.

It is interesting to note from the 1886 minute book of the Lancashire Miners' Federation, that the rate paid at Winstanley No 3 Pit for getting and drawing Orrell Four Feet coal at that time was 1s 8½d (9p) per ton and at Orrell Colliery (Walthew House) No 2 Pit it was 1s 6d (7½p) per ton for both the Orrell Five Feet and Orrell Four Feet Seams.

In the case of the land-owning families, the estate agent or steward was responsible for the working of the collieries, but it is evident from the records that owners such as William Bankes and Meyrick Bankes were well acquainted with all that went on at their collieries. Under the steward came the auditor who was directly responsible for the day-to-day running of the colliery, for the sales of coal at the colliery and the payment of bills. He seems to have been more of a glorified weigh-clerk than a colliery manager, although sometimes, as at Holme's Orrell Colliery, he had considerable financial responsibility only accounting to his employer annually, although he made interim payments to him. In 1769 the Rev Thomas Holme paid his auditor £23 8s (£23.40) per annum, but by 1803 he was receiving £40 a year, and when the colliery closed in 1820 his salary had risen to £50 a year. He does not seem to have gone down the pit except for measuring roads, presumably in regard to yardage and long drawing payments, and for this he was paid an extra 15s (75p) a year.

Some of the colliery owners became quite expert mining engineers simply by learning from their own and other people's mistakes, and by picking up knowledge and gaining experience here and there. John Halliwell was such a one.

Wigan became well known for its expert mechanics during the eighteenth century, one of these being Richard Melling (mentioned in the section on fire engines). Melling was both a surveyor and an engineer and his services seem to have been sought by many of the local colliery owners, especially when they were in trouble. He surveyed the workings and made the plans used in the case between Hawarden and Bankes in 1760. Bradshaigh of Haigh employed him to drain his cannel works, and from Halliwell's journal, it would appear that he was at least consultant to him: 'January 23rd 1759 This day my sons William, Dennis and John went down at the Hollin Hey Pit and came up at the Long Hey Pit being the first time, in company with me and Richard Melling, where we examined all the work'.

Fifty years later, Robert Daglish senior, became more than locally famous as a civil, mechanical and mining engineer, for besides managing the Orrell and Winstanley Collieries for Clarke, he also became consultant civil engineer for several railway companies both in this country and in America. In addition he acted as consultant viewer for many local collieries. His plan of Clarke's Winstanley Collieries dated 1810 and the financial results whilst he was in charge, gives ample testimony to his ability as a colliery manager.

Jonathan Blundell and Son employed Henry Ellam as their colliery manager up to 1788 and paid him a salary of £50 per annum. William Ingold took over from Ellam in that year. In 1796, however, John Harvey was acting in this capacity at a salary of £100 per annum. Ellam was well known as a mining engineer and branched out on his own account with pits at Standish and at other places.

Another local family prominent in colliery management was that of Sherratt. This is a Shropshire-Staffordshire name and they may have originated from that area. A Richard Sherratt was the agent at a colliery at Windle in 1776 and described the cabin there as a 'hovel' a term still used in South Staffordshire when describing a small cabin. In 1781, Thomas Sherratt seems to have been agent at Post House Colliery at Orrell, and the 1790s he was described as the 'Superintendent' there. It was probably Thomas Sherratt's son who later became Blundells' colliery manager and who was subsequently dismissed from that post in 1853 by Armstrong the Newcastle consultant viewer. By that time the usual salary for a colliery manager was £200 per annum.

About the beginning of the nineteenth century some excellent plans were made of some of the larger mines in Orrell showing that mine surveying had by that time become quite advanced. A William Bryham made the plans for Blundells' Edge Hall Colliery and they are of a high standard.

Workshops were established by the large firms and as the works became extensive, it was necessary to employ carpenters, mechanics, saddlers and basket makers as well as blacksmiths: 'In the wood [Dean Wood] October 1775 74 small oak plants [destroyed] where Mr Longbothom is building a smithy and workshop'. Clarke's main workshops were at the Kitt Green end of his estate, near Bell House Farm and adjacent to his wagon road. There was also another workshop at his Winstanley Colliery near the Garden Wood. Stables were built and horsemen were required to look after the many gin horses, cart horses, wagon road horses and, from the early nineteenth century, underground 'galloways'.

Early in the nineteenth century, the practice became common in the district of appointing an 'underlooker' to take charge of the works underground. There must have been an underlooker at Clarke's Winstanley Colliery before 1815, as the story is told in an early Wigan newspaper of him being accosted one night on his way to work by George Lyon the 'highwayman'. Lyon was hanged at Lancaster Castle on the 22 April, 1815. Underlookers were recruited from the ranks of colliers, no doubt from the more sober ones, and up to recent times many colliery undermanagers had worked as colliers in their young days.

Firemen have been mentioned in the section on ventilation. They had charge of the mine, or part of it, under the underlooker. James Corner Superintendent at Blundells Blackrod Colliery, said in 1836 that 'the duties of a fireman are to see that the air is properly circulated and to set the men to work in their respective places'.

Like other areas Orrell suffered its share of dispute and trouble. In April 1792, Henry Blundell, who was Mayor of Liverpool, wrote to William Pitt the Prime Minister about the threat of journeymen carpenters to pull down the houses of people agitating for the abolition of the slave trade, if they were successful in getting the trade abolished. Blundell's house was not threatened, however, as he and his father and brothers were engaged in the trade. He also wrote to Henry Dundas, the Home Secretary, regarding the masters of the coal flats on the rivers and canals:

> There seems to be too general an appearance of discontent amongst all artificers and labourers, which must if possible be prevented spreading into tumult. Annexed is a copy of a note I have this moment received, which comes from a large body of men, and we must either comply with this demand or be guarded against the consequences. The other owners of the collieries and flats in this neighbourhood have received a like notice

> Liverpool 26th May 1792

> The masters of the coal flats in your employ do hereby give notice that they will not proceed in the said flats after the ninth day of June next ensuing, under 1s per ton per trip — which they hope you will agree and consent to give, without any stop being put to the said business, as we are determined not to proceed under that price from that date.

Dundas replied that:

> Although there may not be any immediate disposition to riot amongst these people, it appears from your representation, that you should be watchful of their conduct and that you should pursue every legal and constitutional means of supressing such combinations and bringing the leaders to punishment. From the disposition which has recently been

shown by a certain class of people at Manchester, it is not conceived
to be advisable at this moment to remove any part of the troops now
stationed there from thence, unless in the case of absolute necessity
and if such necessity should hereafter exist, of which you must of course
be the most competent judge, the Commanding Officer at that place
will have instructions to comply with any requisition from you for a
detachment from the forces under his orders.

In the following October there was trouble at the collieries at
Orrell, and Blundell again applied to Dundas for troops:

> The agents from the extensive collieries in the neighbourhood of Wigan
> (and on which the town [Liverpool] depends for its fuel) came this
> evening with the news of the colliers having left their work and collect-
> ed in a riotous manner to the number of near 500, and had been with
> them thus assembled to demand an extravagant advance of wages. They
> had given them only until tomorrow at 3 o'clock to consider of it and
> if their demand is not complied with, they threaten to destroy the
> Works by pulling up the Engines, throwing down the wheels and filling
> up the pits. The consequences to the coal proprietors would be very
> serious, and to the country in general if this combination is not immed-
> iately supressed. I am requested by the coal owners who are now with
> me to entreat of you to give orders to Major Campbell and the Comm-
> anding Officer at Manchester, to march part of their men to Wigan in
> aid of the Magistrates.

Dundas instructed Major Campbell to give 'every assistance in his
power to the Civil Magistrates in preventing any mischief'. He also
remarked that such combinations had lately become so frequent
that it required more than ordinary exertion of the civil power
to supress them and they should enforce the rigid execution of
the law 'against them on whom it can clearly attach'.
  The strikers had only been out for two days when Blundell
again wrote to Dundas:

Liverpool 3rd October 1792

> I returned this morning from Wigan. Our grand object is to save our
> steam engines for drawing the water. No material mischief had been
> done last night, but they threatened much for today if their terms
> were not complied with. A good collier and his drawer can at present
> earn 5sh to 8sh per day between them and if we were to comply with
> their demands, the advance would be nearer to 2sh per day more.

The appearance of the military had the desired affect, and on
10 October the colliers began to return to work. No damage was
done to the engines; they were prevented from working for two
days 'but from which I expect we shall none of us sustain any
material injury'. Many colliers and cannelers from distant works
had 'come to observe the progress of our people and had they
succeeded it would certainly have spread far over this county'.
  The system of binding a collier to a particular coal master for

a definite period was universal throughout Lancashire, and indeed throughout many other coalfields. Small sums of money were given in 'earnest' to the collier on the signing of the bond. Since a minimum period of twelve months residence within a parish entitled the man to parish relief during times of distress, most coal masters preferred that the contract should be for eleven months or less. By this means the collier was prevented, if he was a stranger, from fulfilling his residential qualification for parish relief and, in consequence, from becoming a burden on the local community. Typical local agreements at this time contained such items as the following:

1   The collier to serve the master to the best of his skill and ability for the period stated.

2   The collier must furnish drawers 'to draw the coals to the Eye of the Pitts and there hang or cause to be hung the same upon the hook or hooks and do and perform all other things for making the same ready for raising and winding up out of the said pitt or pitts'.

3   The master on his part contracted to pay a certain sum per work, load or score of baskets, hewn drawn and hung upon the hook ready for winding.

4   If a collier was absent from his work, he had to pay a fine, generally about 1s a day or night and in proportion for a lesser period.

5   Fines were also levied on colliers who holed in the coal instead of the floor or a dirt band in the seam, or who persuaded drawers not to fill the baskets full.

6   All coal had to be sent up 'free from earth, bass, dross, sleck, slags or other rubbidges'.

7   Very heavy fines were imposed on men who did not work according to the liking and satisfaction 'of the steward, agent or underlooker'.

8   The master could demand that the collier worked in the night turn if the occasion was urgent.

9   Long-drawing money was paid generally after 45 or 50yd, and when slack was required, there was a set payment for filling and drawing it to the pit.

10   Concessionary coal was supplied free to every collier.

11   For the supply of way-candles, riddles, sleds, picks, spades and for sharpening the picks, a certain number of baskets had to be supplied free to the owners.

12   On the other hand, the owner allowed baskets to be booked for opening our new places etc.

There are many similarities between old colliers' bonds and modern agreements for strait-work: long-drawing money, and fines for dirty coal for example.

William Harrison, the Relieving Officer for Orrell, Pemberton and UpHolland said in 1842 that the bond system was dying out in his district and most colliers 'are now hired with a fortnights notice'. The system continued in the Northern Coalfield, however, for a further thirty years.

During the famine winter of 1800 serious rioting occurred in the Wigan district, and there were many disturbances during the following twenty years, notably in 1812 and 1819. In 1812 the situation was so serious that a meeting of the Lieutenancy was held in Wigan. The Earl of Derby, the Lord Lieutenant presided, and fifty-six Deputy Lieutenants were present, including Sir William Gerard, Meyrick Bankes, Sir T.D. Hesketh, Sir Richard Clayton, Nicholas Ashton, Isaac Blackburn, George Case, John Clarke, T.S. Standish, R. Willis, J. Walmesley, William Hulton, Michael Hughes and R.G. Hopwood, who had interests in the coal industry. A statement after the meeting said that they viewed

> with horror and extreme sorrow, the riots, tumults and breaches of the peace that have occurred in this County, which disgraced civilised Society and are most dangerous to the Commonwealth or public polity of the Kingdom. Any of His Majesty's subjects may arm themselves and of course may use the ordinary means of force to supress riots and disturbances.

They advised the forming of regular associations for mutual defence. Informers, eager to condemn and expose the rioters were numerous and forthcoming, though their reports were not always relied upon as appears from an editorial in the *Liverpool Mercury* for 22 May 1812:

> The eagerness with which the violence committed by rioters in different districts is exaggerated in the Ministerial papers, frequently attracts our notice. Incidents are given continually before they are authenticated and when authenticated, they are enlarged by additions of extraneous and extravagant falsehood.

The Combination Laws passed in 1800, had been repealed in 1824, but during the twenty-five years of their existence, the colliers had used the many friendly societies as a cloak for trade union activities. At least ten of these societies were operating in Wigan before 1800, and during the period of the Combination Laws, eleven new ones were formed. The Union Society was founded at Orrell on 2 May 1808, and the Brotherly Union Society which functioned at the Ben Jonson Inn Pemberton from October 1794, was active during the whole period of the Combination Laws. There is a record of its rules being altered in October 1804 and again in December 1830.

A colliers' union was formed at Wigan in 1830 and the miners were called out on strike in 1831. There was much unrest as food prices rose, culminating in the great Chartist riots of 1842 when,

on the 12 August, a mob of 10,000 from surrounding areas descended on Wigan, forced their way into the collieries and cotton
mills, stopped the engines and turned 3,000 out of work. By this
time the new Miner's Association of Great Britain and Ireland was
rapidly gaining in strength and funds. It paid £1,000 a year to
William Prowting Roberts, a very able lawyer, to fight its cases.
He was probably responsible for printed addresses from the colliers
employed at the largest collieries in the Wigan area which appeared
before the public during the last weeks of November 1843. One
was composed for the miners of Blundells' Mesnes Cannel Pits.

In November 1844 the following letter was sent to the agent
at Winstanley which seems to indicate that even at that late date
in some cases, the collier had to deliver his coal to the pit shaft:

> Mr Teabey,
> We the colliers in Winstanley under your employ as agreed to ask for
> six to be taken of the score and 3d per yard [to be added] to the coals
> and alf prize of the coals for sleck and way drawing to proposal [pro-
> portion] to the coals as our next neighbouring colliery men [Pember-
> ton Colliery] as been receiving alf price of coals for sleck ever singst
> our price was taken off and they have had 2d per yard more than we
> have had and 3d per score more than we have had and they have sent
> their statement for six to be taken of the score but if this cannot be
> agreed to we then ask for 3d per shilling upon the *field prices at the
> pit shaft.*
> > We remin
> > Your obedent servants in
> > the bond of unity
> The common coal pit men as agreed to ask for the same advance upon
> the field price as the five feet men and six to be taken of the score and
> way drawing in proposal as before and alf price for slack and way draw-
> ing in proposal to the coals.

The signature was a circular stamp with a figure of a heart in
the centre bearing the following words: 'Miners' Association of
Great Britain and Ireland Pemberton District Lancashire'.

Blundells' Orrell Collieries had closed some years before the
date of this letter and Woodcock and Haliburton had ceased operations in Orrell. However, Hustler's and Clarke's pits were still being worked, but as they also came to an end a year or two later,
it is not proposed to pursue this subject any further as it would
no longer be relevant.

ADDRESS

MESSRS. J. BLUNDELL AND SONS.

MESNES, WIGAN, NOVEMBER 20, 1843.

We, the Miners in your employ, beg leave most respectfully to call your attention to the present deplorable condition of ourselves and families, which we know, by sad experience, is mainly attributable to the very scanty pittance we receive as a remuneration for our labour. You are aware that, during the late depression of trade, we bore our privations almost without a murmur, and now that trade is generally admitted to be in an improving condition, we think common justice requires that we should participate in the advantages derivable from such improvements. We do not remind you of the many dangers we have to incur when toiling in the bowels of the earth—nor need we refer to the insalubrious atmosphere we have to breathe, or the unnatural position in which we have to labour; you know these things, at least theoretically, as well as we do. Our object, in presenting you with this short address, is to respectfully, yet firmly, demand a slight augmentation in the scale of prices you are at present paying for the work we perform. In the name of that God, who has declared "the Labourer is worthy of his hire," we ask it on behalf of our once-blooming, but now hunger-stricken and emaciated wives and children; we ask it on behalf of ourselves, who, in many instances, have to descend into the pit without a breakfast, for no other purpose but that you may be able to grow rich, while we hunger and sink by slow degrees into a premature grave.

We, the Miners in the Mesnes, who are employed in getting good strong Cannel, think a man can get ten tubs per day.

PRICES WANTED,

AS THE TUBS STAND NOW :—

Per Tub, for Cannel,	6d.
Per Tub, for Slack,	3d.
In the End,	2s. 0d. per yard.
Drifts,	1s. 0d. per ditto.
Openings,	1s. 8d. per ditto.
Roofing down, as it is,	0s. 6d. per ditto.

Sixty yards from the Pit Shaft, One Penny per Score more; and so on in proportion.

Bottom Day Wage Men, one third added to their present Wages.

Hoping you will comply with this our very moderate request,

We subscribe ourselves,

THE MINERS IN YOUR EMPLOY,

AT THE WIGAN CANNEL WORKS.

THOMAS WALL, PRINTER, MARKET PLACE, WIGAN.

40   Colliers' address to J. Blundell and Sons for an increase in wages, 1843

3.2 THE EMPLOYMENT OF WOMEN AND CHILDREN BELOW GROUND

When Jonathan Blundell & Co took over Jackson's Orrell Colliery in 1776, women and children worked in the mines in the Wigan area for drawing the coal from the collier to the pit shaft or rolley-way, although there is good reason to believe that conditions in Orrell (at least at that time) were not nearly as bad as they became in the Wigan coalfield generally sixty years later.

The writer is acquainted with an old Orrell miner who opened up some of Holme's old Five Feet workings at Orrell for the pur-pose of extracting pillars and, according to him, conditions there at that time were 'bone-dry and comfortable'. The seam was 5ft 3in thick and so the workings would not be too low.

Local pits were only small units then, employing four to six colliers, therefore there would be only about the same number of drawers. It is very probable that the women and children thus em-ployed were the colliers own families. The baskets in use in Blund-ells' pits in the early days had a capacity of 150lb and were not too difficult to handle. Later on however, towards the 1830s many more people were employed in each pit, the pits were deeper and the air often foul because of inadequate ventilation. Baskets be-came very much larger – up to 5cwt – although by that time wheel-trams had come into use. Generally speaking, conditions became such as to lead to the brutalisation and degradation of the collier population.

An article in the *Gentleman's Magazine* entitled 'the Lancashire Collier Girl' describes conditions in the Orrell district in 1795. The colliery referred to was very probably Halliwell's Fire Engine Colliery. John Hodson, the father of the girl referred to (Betty Hodson) took her and her brother to work with him in the pit when she was nine and her brother seven:

> These little folks soon put their strength to the basket, dragging the coals from the workmen to the pit and by these efforts did the duty as it is called of one drawer. It is with pride that we make it known to little children that Betty and her brother at an early age cleared their parents seven shillings a week. Here was a treasure and satisfaction they were taught to feel by example and by the encouragement given to them.

One wonders if the pride of the man who wrote this would have been so great if his own little children were 'putting their strength to the basket'. He then goes on to describe the death of the father who, when he was hooking a basket on to the rope at the bottom

of the shaft, was killed by stones falling from the top. A John
Hodson is recorded as working at Halliwell's Colliery for several
years and in August 1776 was working in the Know Pit as a collier. In the following August an inquest was held on John Hodson
'accidentally killed at Orrell'. Besides John Hodson, Thomas, William and Joshua Hodson worked as colliers for Halliwell, and indeed one of the pits was known as 'Hodson's Pit', probably because they sank it. After the father's death the mother became
mentally deranged and was for five years maintained by the parish.
Two of the boys aged seven and nine were apprenticed by the parish, and two younger ones were also taken care of.

> At her father's death, Betty was between eleven and twelve years old
> and she continued in the coal pit in preference to throwing herself on
> the parish, as she was then, by her own labour, capable of earning a
> shilling a day. At her full strength she got 2/6d and at sixteen took her
> mother to live with her.

She also nursed her two brothers during some months of illness until they died, and at the age of eighteen she buried her
mother. At no time did she apply to the parish for relief. Over-
work, worry and grief, and most likely lack of sufficient food,
brought on a breakdown in her health and she was compelled to
give up her employment.

Hearing of an underservant's place at nearby Winstanley Hall, she
made application for it. Girls from collieries were not looked on
with favour for domestic service as they were usually rough in
language, manner and appearance and not much given to the domestic arts. However, enquiries were made at the colliery where she
had worked and the manager said

> as they often in the mines laboured by task work, she has overpowered
> herself, and that she was as good a girl as any alive, and was both be-
> loved and protected by the colliers, who were sometimes quarrelsome
> when relaxing over their cups, but howsoever, they would never let
> anyone say improper things or offer harm to a woman in the pits.

This report is the antithesis of the description given by the commissioner in 1842, of the treatment of women in the pits of the
Wigan area.

Betty was taken on at Winstanley by William Bankes, who was
noted for his kindness to the poor of the locality. She eventually
became the cook at Winstanley Hall and together with other ser-
vants received a legacy of £50 on the death of Mr Bankes. It
might be expected that Betty would be deformed with such excess of manual labour at so early an age, but she is described as

well looking, tall and slender in person, with grey eyes and a bold countenance — but it is the boldness of honesty — she still maintains that fearless character of the miner whom no dangers can possibly daunt.

The system of employing women and children underground continued for almost another fifty years. Very young boys were used for opening and closing air doors when the drawers came through with their tubs or baskets. The occupation was described as one of the most pitiable in a coal pit for its extreme monotony: 'Were it not for the passing and repassing of the wagons, it would be equal to solitary confinement of the worst order'.

Mr E.W. Binney FRS at a meeting of the Manchester Geological Society in Wigan in 1871, said very great changes had taken place since he came to the district.

Within a short distance of this place in this County, there were former-ly thousands of women employed in carrying coal and at the instance of Lord Shaftesbury and Mr Brotherton, I went down numerous pits to get drawings of the women to show how they were employed. It was astonishing and wonderful to me to see the power which some of these women had in drawing the corves in which the coal was conveyed. The women went on all fours with a chain or rope passed round their necks and under their bodies and by this means they dragged the corves in something the same way as bullocks would. The immense power which was developed in the limbs of some of these women was indeed won-derful. It is singular to think that it is not thirty years since in this district, thousands of women were employed in such work and the greater part of the coal wrought in Lancashire, was conveyed along the bottom of the mines by women on all fours. Though I was partly in-strumental in getting the employment of women in this degrading fash-ion put an end to, the measure caused a great deal of trouble and I must admit, was accompanied by much individual hardship.

Some of the women earned excellent wages and when the Act came into operation, the deprivation of employment caused much suffering. Three or four years after the Act had been passed, I was going one day from Ince to Wigan, when I met a woman who had just got out of a pit. I said to her 'I thought they did not allow you to work in the pit now' and she said 'No, they dunnot, but one gets down on the sly. I cannot see that I am not so well employed there as anywhere else. I cannot see why women should not conduct themselves in pits as well as in factories. I have an old woman at home to support; I wish those chaps that got the women taken out of the pits would pay me the 3s a week less wages which I get now'. She had been used to getting 11s a week before but after the Act was passed, as she could only work 'on the sly' her wages were reduced to 8s a week. It was a pity to take them out of the pits so suddenly.

Kennedy, the commissioner sent by the government to enquire into the condition of women and children in the pits in Lanca-shire, paid a visit to Blundells' Cannel Pits on the Mesnes at Wigan.

He interviewed the under-looker and several of the children there and although this is not one of the Orrell Pits the conditions would be very similar to those in the Orrell Four Feet Seam if not better, as the Orrell pits were coming to the end of their life and Mesnes Colliery was new:

Jonathan Blundell's Mesnes Colliery, Wigan
May 10th, 1841
No. 38
John Houghton, underlooker to Mr Blundell, Wigan Mesnes, May 10th 1841.

"You are the underlooker at this pit?"

"Yes, I am".

"How many women are employed at this pit?"

"We have only three or four, but we have a good many girls and boys".

"Do you prefer employing females in the pit?"

"No, I don't, pits are not fit places for women, they hear a great deal of coarse talk and get into the way of using bad language to each other".

"What kind of wives do women make who have been brought up in the collieries?"

"Why, I married my wife out of the pit, and her father and mother before her worked in the pit; they were both burned to death, but I think it would have been better for her if she had never been in at all. She has never been in one since I married her, but I don't think they can be expected to keep a house as well as those who have been brought up to it. You shall see mine and then you can judge for yourself; but there is the greatest difference in them — some will keep their homes very well and others as dirty as can be. Some will gather a bit of furniture together and others will not have a stool to sit down on".

"How are colliers as regards personal cleanliness?"

"There is a great difference in that too; some take pains to keep themselves clean, but a great many are very dirty and scarcely ever wash their bodies".

"There seems to be a great want of education!"

"Yes, that is very much wanted, very few colliers have learned to read and write. I never went to school myself, but my master thought fit to make me his underlooker and I learned to read and write since then".

No. 39

Betty Houghton, waggoner, Mr Blundell's mine Wigan Mesnes. May 11th, 1841.

"What age are you?"

"Nearly fifteen".

"When did you first begin work?"

"I have been between five and six years in the pits".

"You are a waggoner I believe?"

"Yes, I am".

"Do you use the belt and chain?"

"No, there is no belt and chain work in this pit, the coal is all waggoned".

"What time do you go to work in the morning?"

"At six o'clock".

"Do you stop for breakfast?"

"Sometimes we do for a quarter of an hour".

"Do you stop for dinner?"

"Yes, an hour from twelve to one".

"Is this full hour always taken for dinner time?"

"Yes, mostly".

"What time do you come up at night?"

"Between five and six o'clock". (It was half past five when this was taken).

"Do you like this employment?"

"No. I don't so well. I would rather work above, but I am 'liked' (obliged) to like it".

"Have you ever been to school? Can you read or write?"

"I can read i'th Testament, but I cannot write; I wish I could".

No. 40 Ellen Taylor at the same place May 11th 1841.

"What age are you?"

"Eleven years old".

"How long have you been in the pits?"

"About four years".

"Do you attend church or chapel?"

"Yes".

"Do you go to Sunday School?"

"Yes, sometimes".

"Have you ever been to a day school?"

"Yes".

"Can you read and write?"

"I can read but I cannot write".

"Do you ever get beaten?"

"No, not i'th pit but my mother beats me sometimes when I'm nought". (naughty)

No 41 Thomas Parkinson at the same place. May 11th 1841

"What age are you?"

"Nearly sixteen".

"What time do you get into the pit in the morning?"

"At six o'clock and I come out at half past five and six sometimes".

"What wages can you earn per week?"

"Seven shillings".

"Do you attend any Sunday School?"

"No".

"Have you ever been to a day school?"

"No".

"Can you read or write?"

"No, neither the one nor t'other".

No. 42 Betsy Lowe at the same place May 11th 1841

"What age are you?"

"Fourteen years old".

"How long have you been at work?"

"Three years".

"You work the same hours as the other waggoners in this pit?"

"Yes, I do".

"Do you attend a Sunday School?"

"No, I don't".

"Have you ever been to school?"

"No".

"Do you attend church or chapel. Can you read or write?"

"No".

The hours of work at the pits were never less than twelve, and indeed were sometimes more during the eighteenth century. A letter in *Lloyd's Evening Post* in the 1770s mentions the terribly long hours worked by some miners:

> Cut off from the light of Heaven for sixteen or seventeen hours a day, they are obliged to undergo a drudgery which the veriest slave in the plantations would think intolerable.

By 1840, a twelve-hour shift with an hour's break for dinner, was the rule in the Wigan area and as late as 1886, Blundells' Queen and Bye Pits worked twelve-hour shifts and the King Pit eleven-hour shifts.

3.3 LIVING CONDITIONS, HOUSING, EDUCATION AND RELIGION

Edward Hall, in *Miss Weeton's Journal of a Governess, 1811-1825,* mentioning the newly-formed Far Moor Chapel, says:

> Farr Moor is situated at a little over a mile distant from UpHolland and a more debased, vulgar, brutal district for his ministry [Mr Holgate's] could hardly have been his lot. Illiterate miners and weavers

just emerging from the barbarism of the eighteenth century and their slightly worse womenfolk form his congregation. As regards Miss Weeton's alternative choice, — Lamberhead Green and its Methodism, — this district was as sunk in besotted ignorance as Farr Moor.

Twenty years later, the living conditions and habits of the mining population in Orrell and Pemberton were described by the Rev Joshua Paley, the incumbent of St John's Church, Pemberton. Although he had four Sunday Schools and three Day Schools, with a fourth Day School under construction, he said: 'The habits of these men, especially the colliers, are so bad that the utmost difficulties are thrown in our way of communicating instruction'. Public houses and beer shops were open most of the day; sick and burial clubs and other societies had their headquarters there, and whole families were very often 'found together in these places of iniquity'. He goes on to say that 'There is generally awful profligacy amongst the colliers and it always happens that in such matters, the children and young people imitate their example'. He found this with both sexes and early on the children became habituated to scenes of drunkenness and obscenity. In Lamberhead Green and Orrell there were more than forty public houses as late as sixty years ago.

Very few collier's houses had more than one bedroom, and often a whole family, if not more than one, slept in one room: 'There is no delicacy observed in this, which of course has a bad effect on the morals'.

After working in the pits, the children were seldom fit for any other occupation and the women in general knew no habits of household economy. A large proportion of the evils that prevailed were due to the women being absent from their homes and working in the pits. Mr Paley was sure that education of the children was the only remedy, but although he had a night school, in each of his four districts, the young people were so tired with work that comparatively few attended. Education in the district was not free and there was so much poverty, often the result of intemperance, that the colliers could not pay for the children to be educated. Only the Sunday Schools were free and here the children might pick up a few well-selected crumbs of knowledge such as would teach them to be honest and obedient, to know their place and be content in it, to honour and respect their superiors and to serve their masters with all their strength and diligence. Some well disposed persons had supported a Sunday School at Lamberhead Green many years before St John's Church was founded as the following letter shows:

Winstanley Hall
Feb 13, 1797

Lamberhead Green Sunday School

As there has been no general meeting for more than two years, Mr Bankes informs the subscribers to Lamberhead Green Sunday School that the average number of scholars has been about sixty and that they have attended regularly. But Mr Bankes is of the opinion that the average is not in proportion to the population of the place.

Mr Bankes likewise represents that this school from the non-residence of the subscribers labours very peculiarly under the inconvenience of want of inspection and superintendance and he freely owns that he does not like all the responsibility attaching to himself — he therefore proposes a general meeting of the subscribers on the first Friday in July to take this and other metters into consideration.

Mr Bankes also represents that the subscriptions for some years have been irregularly paid and that not only the interest on the subscriptions is lost but also when the subscriptions have been paid late in the year, it gives then an appearance of belonging to the subsequent year. by which means and by death it has happened that more than one subscription has been totally lost.

Mr Bankes wishes that the original mode of paying the subscriptions annually into Mr Doncaster's bank at Lady Day should be again adopted and therefore proposes that the subscribers would by themselves their friends or their agents pay their subscriptions regularly into the said bank on the 25th March in each year.

William Bankes

Treasurer

Besides the Anglican Church of St John at Pemberton (built in 1832) and the RC Church of St James in Orrell (built in 1798), there were several non-conformist chapels in Pemberton and Orrell at this period, and we can hardly accept the foregoing description as applicable to the entire working population in the area. Foremost among the non-conformist chapels, was the Wesleyan Chapel at Lamberhead Green founded in 1796, thirty-six years before the Anglican Church. Wesley himself is said to have been to Pemberton during one of his Wigan visits.

Contemporary descriptions of events like the Lamberhead Green Fair indicate that not everyone spent the whole of his spare time in the alehouse. Seven or more brass bands from the surrounding districts joined in the 'imposing' processions of the friendly societies, so we must infer that these bandsmen spent at least some of their time acquiring a knowledge of music. The fair was a great local event, at which the stalls occupied the whole of Chapel Street, and stretched across the main Ormskirk Road on to the Pole Hillock.

In 1834, young Meyrick Bankes who had succeeded to the Winstanley estate a few years earlier, made a survey of his property in Winstanley, Orrell, Pemberton, Billinge and UpHolland. At that time, he owned about a quarter of the land in the five townships and it may be assumed that conditions on the estate were fairly typical of the whole area. He mentions six cottages as 'dirty, nasty cottages –should come down', twelve dirty cottages, eighteen small cottages with one small bedroom, twenty-six with two or more bedrooms and thirteen 'good comfortable cottages'. Some of those with only one bedroom had a parlour and buttery as well as a kitchen downstairs.

Of the thirteen early nineteenth-century cottages, previously owned by Blundells in Orrell, which have survived, five contain four rooms, seven have five rooms and one has six. There was no organised system of sewage disposal and water for drinking and washing was generally obtained from rain-water butts, wells, ponds, streams, old pit shafts and ditches. Lamberhead Green was supplied with water from the Pingot Well sunk by the Bankes family and half a mile from the village. As late as the 1870s carters were charging 1d for four gallons of water delivered in the village, otherwise it had to be carried in pails. Many local women did their washing in the delivery trough of Clarke's pumping engine in the Pingot before the main line railway was constructed there, as many as two hundred being there at the same time.

In their liesure time the colliers indulged in a number of sports. In the barbarous method of fighting, known as 'purring' the combatants kicked one another with their specially pointed clogs, as well as punching one another with their fists: 'When one has the other down on the ground, he first endeavours to choke him by squeezing his throat and then kicks him on the head and body with his clogs'. Wrestling superceded 'purring' in the second half of the nineteenth century, the Lancashire 'Catch-as-Catch-Can' style being generally used. Also the colliers liked to attend race meeting at Newton and other places, for, unlike many of their descendants today, they were averse to patronising a sport they could not see. 'Piggy' or 'Knurr and Spell' matches were very popular as well as bowling and field bowling, Whippet-racing, rabbit-coursing round the 'wall-side' at Winstanley Park, as well as pigeon-flying (racing) and starling shooting, all had their followers. Pitch-and-toss was played on most Sunday mornings well into this century at a spot near the Blundell Arms at Pemberton, a constant watch being kept for the local constable.

3.4 ACCIDENTS

The first Government inspectors to inspect and report on underground workings were appointed in 1850. Before that date no
proper records were kept of fatal accidents at the various collieries. The records of the coroner's inquisitions are very incomplete;
in fact some of them consist of nothing more than bills for expenses incurred by the coroner, mentioning the name of the de-
ceased without giving any further information. Similarly there are
no Wigan newspapers covering the early part.of the period. However, one finds odd entries like the one in the Pemberton Constable's Book dated 27 July 1814 when they paid expenses 'for an
inquest on seven persons killed in Mr Woodcock's pit'.

An old notebook kept by one John Ainscough, who worked for
Jonathan Blundell and Son at the beginning of the nineteenth
century, and who lies buried next to George Lyon, the 'Highwayman' in UpHolland churchyard, has been handed down in the
Ainscough and Fairhurst families of Orrell. This sheds a little light
on the subject of accidents, but whether these were all the fatal
accidents at Blundells' pits or at all the local pits, we do not know.
Ainscough gives the names of fifty persons who were killed between February 1819 and February 1826. Six of these were wom-
en and two were young boys. Nine met their deaths by drowning
(presumably by an inundation of water from old workings) and
ten were burned to death, no doubt in explosions of firedamp.

The coroner's bills for expenses for the 8½ years between December 1828 and July 1837 are a little more informative than
usual. During that period inquests held in the townships of Orrell,
Winstanley, Pemberton, UpHolland and Shevington (parts of all
of which are in the Orrell coal belt) gives the following information:

| | Number Killed | | |
Cause of Death	Males	Females	Total
'Falling down a coal pit'	13	3	16
'Coals falling on him in a coal pit'	4		4
'Explosion of inflammable air in a coal pit'	48	14	62
'Killed in a coal pit' (probably from falls of roof)	12	3	15
'Tub falling on him in a coal pit'	2		2
'Falling off a stage at a coal pit'	1		1
'Killed by wheels of a coal waggon passing over him'	1		1
Totals	81	20	101

Three major explosions took place. The first on 26 April 1830 when nine men were killed; the second on 26 April 1831 which killed seventeen men and the third on 19 December in the same year when a further twenty-eight men were killed. William Harrison, the Relieving Officer for Pemberton, Orrell and UpHolland, said in 1842:

> We have had as many as twenty-eight people killed at one time by an explosion of firedamp and eighteen at another and often large numbers killed. They [the colliers] are very reckless.

At the same period, the Rev Joshua Paley, the Minister at Pemberton, said:

> there are very few families in which one or more deaths have not occurred from accidents in the pits, in many, three or four have died thus. Few weeks pass in which some awful occurrence does not take place. Indeed it is môst lamentable and shocking to consider the scenes that are continually presented to me from such accidents and they are continually occurring.

The inquest returns seem to confirm the Rev Paley's remark about several having been killed in some families. For example in the explosion of 26 April 1830, Robert, John and Betty Mollineux were killed; in the explosion of 26 February 1831 John, Thomas, James, Charles and Fanny Ainscough were killed as well as James Atherton and James Atherton the younger. Again in the explosion which occurred in the following December, James, John, Thomas, Joseph and Ann Berry were killed and a Thomas Ainscough who may have been of the same family as the Ainscoughs killed in the previous explosion. Perhaps the John Ainscough killed in February was the one who kept the notebook mentioned above.

A few examples of accidents at some of Blundells' pits towards the end of our period may serve to illustrate the situation at that time. The explosion which occurred on 4 April 1830 was caused by an air door being left open on the previous night causing gas to accumulate and this was ignited by a naked light carried by a miner going to his working place. At another of Blundells' pits, eleven persons were killed including at least one woman and another eight badly burned on 6 October 1836. Again on 12 October 1839 it was reported that an incident had occurred:

> that had been nearly attended with loss of life in a pit belonging to R.B.H. Blundell Esq. called the 'Adventure Pit' on last Monday afternoon. An explosion of firedamp took place and although a great number of men were employed, only two received any injury and that so slight that they will be enabled to resume their work in a few days.

Five years later at another of their pits, two men were killed and eight badly burned after an eruption of water and gas – the gas being ignited by workmen passing at the time.

Many accidents occurred in shafts. On 12 June 1839, William Spencer employed at Messrs Blundells' New Pit fell out of a basket while ascending. He was found dead at the bottom of the pit with his heels uppermost, his head being immersed in water and both arms being dreadfully fractured. Eighteen years later, two men had a miraculous escape in Blundells' Number Nine Pit when the winding engine drum came out of gear, the rope broke and the basket with the two men in it dropped 210ft down the shaft: 'Fortunately the men laid themselves down in the basket and were little injured except shook. I took them both home and the Dr was there also'.

Boiler explosions became very frequent especially as working pressures rose. An example of this occurred when Robert Barker met his death in 1808. The inquest was on 10 June 1808 before William Eccles, Mayor of Wigan and coroner:

> The said Robert Barker came to his death being then and there tending and taking care of a certain steam engine there situate and the Pan or Boiler belonging to the said Engine being then and there charged and filled with a large quantity of Hot Water Steam and Vapour, it so happened that the said Pan or Boiler, by the quantity force and violence of the said Hot Water Steam and Vapour was then and there accidentally, casually and by misfortune, burst and the said Hot Water Steam and Vapour issued thereout to end upon the said Robert Barker, who was then standing near to the said Pan by reason whereof the body of the said Robert Barker was scalded and burnt.

As always, falls of roof took a heavy and regular toll and there were many deaths from this cause.

During this period 1838-50 the coroner's bills for expenses show only the names of those killed. No information is given as to the cause of death, but there are instances where long lists of names are given for inquests on the same date and in the same place and these look suspiciously like mining accidents, but we can not be sure. It is very probable that the fatal accident rate was worse during this period than in any previous one, as it was due to public concern that the Mines' Inspectorate was established in 1850.

Apart from the recorded fatal accidents, there must have been many cases of people being maimed for life in the pits of the Orrell-Pemberton district. There were no hospitals where such accident cases could receive attention. It was due mainly to public concern again, that institutions like the Wigan Infirmary were established. There had been a Public Dispensary in Wigan for many years when the following was recorded in the Dispensary Committee Minute Book in 1866:

> Your committee are fully convinced that great necessity exists in Wigan and the neighbourhood for an institution to which accident cases can be taken and attended to. They are satisfied that large numbers of patients of this class die or are disabled for life, through want of proper nursing, which is not obtainable in the majority of the homes of the working classes and that many families are made paupers in consequence.

It was reported that if the people of Wigan erected an infirmary for this purpose, the Mansion House Committee would make a handsome contribution to the funds. Several of the local coal proprietors had served on the Dispensary Committee for many years, prominent among them being Thomas and Edward Woodcock and Alexander Haliburton.

CHAPTER FOUR

The Principal Colliery Concerns

4.1 THE JACKSON-BLUNDELL COLLIERIES

John Jackson's colliery on his portion of the Saltersford or Orrell House estate, as it is now known, was described in 1738 as being 'the most contiguous to the river of any yet opened'. Jackson, a watchmaker, owned twelve Cheshire acres equal to 25.3 statute acres of this estate. In July 1738 he entered into an agreement with Alexander Leigh and Robert Holt, the undertakers of the Douglas Navigation, to supply them with the entire output of his colliery once the Navigation was completed until he had delivered the quantity of 800,000 baskets of riddled coal, each basket to contain: 'six score twelve pounds customary weight, at the least', ie 132lb.

The coal was to be delivered to a coal yard to be made on the banks of the Douglas at Gathurst at a price of 3s 2d (16p) per score of twenty baskets, this number of baskets being equal in weight to just over 1 ton 3cwt. Therefore the price was 2s 8½d (13½p) per ton. Jackson was to be paid for each quantity of coal not later than three months after it was delivered to Gathurst.

At the time the agreement was signed, he had expressed his relief that 'he should thereby be free from the trouble of going abroad to collect the money for his coal as he used to do which has been very troublesome and expensive to him'. However, he asked to be able to continue his sales as he had done formerly until the Navigation was opened. By the time it was opened in 1742, his usual sales must have become more profitable to him as he was very dilatory with the deliveries of coal to Gathurst. Instead, he was sending coal by land carriage to Poulton and other parts of the Fylde, the very markets the river proprietors intended catering for: 'When the Navigation should be completed the chief trade would consist chiefly in the carriage of coal to the Fylde and other northern parts'.

Not only did Jackson lag behind in the quantity of coal he supplied, but the quality left much to be desired. It was badly riddled and much of it consisted of 'sleck and culm'. The river proprietors also had doubts as to whether Jackson had enough coal under his twelve Cheshire acres to supply 800,000 baskets as this was not a large area and the colliery had been worked for very many years before this time. Even before the Earl of Derby sold the Manor in 1597, it had been agreed that the tenants of Saltersford pits should pay him £5 a year rent but also they should pay Robert Leigh, the subordinate landlord, 11s 6d (57½p) on every hundred baskets raised. In the 1740s, the only seam worked at Saltersford was the Orrell Five Feet. On that estate it consisted of two leaves, the top one 2ft 9in thick and the lower one 1ft 10in. A 6in dirt band intervened. Altogether there were 47in of coal and in a seam of this thickness there would be 14,666 tons in one Cheshire acre or 175,992 tons in twelve acres. Taking a figure of 60 per cent extraction, which is based on the 4yd square pillars and 5ft wide straits or roadways found in Holme's workings in the same seam in the adjoining estate, 105,595 tons would be available originally. 800,000 baskets of the capacity stated is equal to 46,875 tons, so it is possible that Jackson had enough coal – depending on how much had been worked in the past – to fulfil his commitment. The proprietors wanted to know how many baskets there were in an acre 'allowing for the pillars necessary to be left for support of the roof'.

The result of the complaint of the river proprietors to the Earl of Cholmondeley, Chancellor of the County of Palatine of Lancaster, was that Jackson was ordered to supply 48,000 baskets of coal per annum to the Navigation. This amounts to 2,829 tons each year. Presumably, any tonnage raised by him over and above that figure could be disposed of by land sale as he had done previously. An item in the Douglas Navigation accounts dated 20 November 1748 states that the 'costs in Chancery against Jackson when he refused to supply us with coal' amounted to £41 7s (£41.35). It is small wonder that the proprietors took him to Court, for between 15 March 1743 and that date, Jackson had been paid £430 16s 4½d (£430.82) for coal supplied and this is equal to only 54,430 baskets in 5½ years out of the 800,000 he had contracted to supply.

Presumably Jackson completed his contract as he was still sending 48,000 baskets a year to the river in the late 1750s and he seems to have acquired the coal, if not the surface, of the whole Saltersford estate which is about 51 Cheshire acres. A datestone now in the garden of Orrell House has the inscription 'John and Cicely Jackson 1737'. That he was a man of some importance locally is signified by the fact that the main road from the Old Engine public house to Gathurst Brow was known as Jackson's Lane until recent years and his name appears amongst the original list of shareholders in the Leeds and Liverpool Canal.

He continued working his colliery, the northern area of his work-

41   Blundells' Orrell House Farm

ings being originally de-watered by soughs into the brook at Dean Wood until, to work the coal to the dip of this sough level, he was forced to sink a pumping or engine pit which was fitted up with bucket pumps operated by a water wheel.

In the 1770s Jackson erected a 'Fire Engine' of the Newcomen type no doubt to sink to the Orrell Four Feet Seam which lay at a depth of 63yd below the Five Feet then being worked. On the 23 December 1774 the following advertisement appeared in the *Liverpool General Advertiser:*

ORRELL COAL MINE

TO BE SOLD (at the Bears Paw in Wigan on January 18th) The Mine or Delf of coal under 20 acres of land (old measure) lying in Orrell in this County being part of a large estate called Salters Ford, the inheritance of Michael Jackson of Orrell aforesaid, Gentleman. This part of the estate, under which the mine is intended to be sold, lies about 100 rods from the new canal to Liverpool; and the River Douglas (which communicates with the sea) and from which there is a gradual descent. There is a Fire Engine on the other part of the premises which it may reasonably be presumed will effectually drain the water from the mine intended to be sold and of which the purchaser may have the benefit according to the conditions of sale. This mine which is now in work in the other part of the estate is four feet and upwards thick and in this place to enumerate the amazing qualities of the coals and the profits made of the culm and the slack arising therefrom would be superfluous; especially as proofs have been so often made in so many parts of this County to give them a preference...The premises as also the works daily carrying on in three different shafts or pits in the other part of the property may be viewed by applying to Mr Jackson at his house in Orrell.

Michael was the son of John Jackson and he was trying to raise money on his twenty Cheshire acres of the Orrell Five Feet Seam in his property. No mention is made of the lower seam, the Orrell Four Feet, which was 3ft 6in thick.

Apparently none of the prospective buyers were interested in the twenty acres and it was thought that if the whole estate and colliery was put up for auction, it would be a more attractive proposition. Thus it was that another advertisement appeared in the same paper six weeks later:

ORRELL COAL MINE

The sale of that part of this mine which is the inheritance of Mr Michael Jackson of Orrell and lately advertised in this paper, being postponed on account of a number of gentlemen declining to purchase part of it without the whole. THEREFORE NOTICE IS HEREBY GIVEN, that the whole mine now in work under 51 acres of land, together with the Fire Engine and all other materials whatsoever used in working the said mine (and of which a proper inventory will be produced at the time of sale) to be sold at auction at the Bears Paw in Wigan on the 24th February.

This advertisement was also abortive and Jackson remained in possession, although it is difficult to understand why the colliery remained unsold just at the time the canal was opened. However, events were taking place in Liverpool which were eventually to decide the ownership of Saltersford for the next century and three quarters.

On the 1 April 1774, Jonathan Blundell, William Earle, Samuel Warren and Edward Chaffers all of Liverpool, the first two having been prominent in promoting the construction of the Lancashire end of the Leeds and Liverpool Canal:

agreed to become partners for the space of ten years as well in the buying of coal and cannel at and from the several mines near the River Douglas and in carrying the same in flats, barges or other boats and vessels by means of that Navigation and the Leeds Canal to Liverpool for the sale and disposal thereof at Liverpool.

They purchased two closes of land at the top of Old Hall Street Liverpool and sold a portion of it to the canal proprietors for the construction of a basin, quays, and landing places but they reserved the greater portion to themselves and at the southern end they:

erected a weighing engine, counting house and other conveniences and made a cut or sluice to connect into the said basin, with pathways and landing place and walled the same round at considerable expense for their coalyard.

Their business prospered well and on the 27 January 1775, they were able to advertise as follows in the *Liverpool General Advertiser:*

Messrs Warren and Co [Warren, Blundell, Earle and Chaffers] beg leave to return thanks to the public for the great encouragement they have received and inform them that they have now got a sufficient quantity of COAL and CANNEL into their yard at the bason of the Liverpool and Leeds Canal where they may depend upon being served with honour on the following terms for ready money only viz:-

Best Douglas House Coal at 7s 6d per load of 20 cwts of 120lbs each

Best Smiths Coal at 10s per load of 20 cwts of 140 lbs each

Best Wigan Cannel Coal at 14s 6d per 20 cwts of 120 lbs each

Small Wigan Cannel Coal at 11s 0d per 20 cwts of 120 lbs each

Laid down in any part of this town free of cartage; each load weighed at their machine and a ticket sent by the carter:

And for the accommodation of the poor a person attends constantly in the yard to deliver them hundred or half hundred-weights at the undermentioned prices:

House coals at 4½d for 120 lbs
Large Cannel at 8½d for 120 lbs
Small Cannel at 6½d for 120 lbs

They probably purchased much of their coal from Jackson's colliery but on the 6 March 1776 they entered into an agreement with Michael Jackson for the purchase of all the coals produced at his colliery. That Jackson had now sunk to the Orrell Four Feet is indicated by the fact that 'Douglas House Coals' are advertised as well as 'Smith Coals', house coals being Orrell Four Feet and Smiths Coals Orrell Five Feet.

To facilitate the transport of this coal they lost no time in constructing a wagon road from Jackson's colliery through Dean Wood to the canal. This was probably the first wagon road or tram road in Orrell, and they mention this in the second advertisement on 1 November 1776:

Messrs Warren and Co [Warren, Blundell, Earle and Chaffers] beg leave to acquaint the Public THAT they have completed a waggon road from Mr Jackson's Coal Mines in Orrell (near Wigan) down to the Canal by which means Coal is brought down to their Yard in Liverpool, without being subject to so much breakage as those from other Mines upon the said Canal. That they now have and will continue to have in their yard, a large quantity of fresh House Coal, Smith Coal and Cannel at the undermentioned prices:

Best Douglas House Coal 6s 10d per ton of 2,400 lbs	Carting
Best Smiths Coal 9s 4d per ton of 2,800 lbs	8d per
Best Cannel 7d per cwt or 12s 6d per ton of 2,400 lbs	ton

In July of the same year, Jonathan Blundell had purchased Chaffer's share in their coal merchants business. Chaffers had previously sold a quarter of his share to Ambrose Lace, but Blundell purchased this also. Warren had sold half of his share to Thomas

Birch, but William Earle retained his, thus, although the firm was known as Warren & Co, Blundell had at this early stage acquired a half share in the business, Earle having a quarter share with Warren and Birch one eighth share each. A valuation at this time shows that they had spent £1,600 on the land in Liverpool, including the coal yard, quays, counting house etc and £180 on 'Flats, barges, boats and other vessels'.

At the same time as they made the agreement with Jackson, they also made a contract with Holt Leigh, James Hodson and Thomas Doncaster, goldsmith, all of Wigan that they should supply 'at the Eyes of the Cannel Pits in Aspull and Ince, 38,500 score of good Roan marketable and saleable Round Cannel' at the rate of 2,000 scores of baskets per year. Each score was to consist of twenty-four baskets and each basket to contain 124lb weight.

They carried on in this way until the following advertisement appeared in Williamson's *Liverpool Advertiser* for 27 April 1780:

COLLIERY
to be sold by auction

At the house of Mr Dale, known by the name of George's Coffee House, near the EXCHANGE in Liverpool, the following premises, late the estate of Michael Jackson of Orrell near Wigan a bankrupt, on Monday the 15th day of May next at 3 o'clock in the afternoon.

The Fee-Simple and Inheritance of and in all that substantial and well built Messuage or dwellinghouse, buildings, Gardens, and Premises of him the said Michael Jackson, pleasantly situated in Orrell aforesaid, now in his possession, together with fourteen other dwellinghouses near unto the same, and the several closes, closures or parcels of land thereunto belonging, and the valuable Coal Mines under the same (having a close communication with the Leeds Canal, from whence coals are easily shipt for Liverpool) all of which lands contain, in the whole by common estimation, 49 acres, or thereabouts, be the same more or less.

These lands are subject to the following incumbrances, viz. an annuity of £60 a year for an Old Life of upwards of Sixty five, to an Annuity of £20 a year, during the life of the aforesaid person's wife (in case she survives him) aged 60 years and an Annuity of £20 a year to the wife of the said Michael Jackson, (in case she survives him) now aged 36 years and upwards and a chauntery rent of £10 a year for ever.

Also at the same time and place will be Sold by Auction, 28 Horses, 13 Coal Waggons, with iron Wheels, sundry Implements belonging to a Fire Engine, 3 6in wheel Carts, 1 Waggon with broad and narrow wheels, 1 Lime Waggon, 1 weigh engine and weights, the utensils of a smith's shop, some boring augers, and some timbers.

For further particulars thereof, apply to Mr William Collinson at Warren & Co Coal Yard or Mr James Sudell, Attorney in Liverpool. A plan of the Premises, may be seen at the time of the Sale, or by applying as above.

It is rather puzzling that the fire engine which worked the pumps

42 Jonathan Blundell, 1723-1800   43 Henry Blundell, 1755-1832
   (Bluecoat School, Liverpool)   *(Bluecoat School, Liverpool)*

seems to be excluded from the sale, although if that had been sold separately to some other party for removal elsewhere, it would greatly detract from the value of the colliery.

Jonathan Blundell purchased the estate, which continued in his family until the death of Major Cuthbert L.B.H. Blundell in 1947. Shortly after the purchase, Jonathan and his son Henry purchased the remaining shares in the coal business from Earle, Warren and Birch and from 1784, if not earlier, it went under the name of Jonathan Blundell and Son and the firm continued under this name until 1900 when the family formed a private limited company known as the 'Pemberton Colliery Co Ltd — late Jonathan Blundell and Son'.

It may be worth while digressing a little to show what kind of a background the Blundell family had. Jonathan Blundell's father, Alderman Bryan Blundell, merchant and master mariner had been one of the most successful sea captains of the day in Liverpool, owning his own vessels and he was said to be the 'greatest shallop racer from the Mersey to the West Indies'. Three of his vessels the *Mulberry,* the *Batchelor* and the *Robert* were reputed to be the first vessels to enter the 'Old Dock', Liverpool's first dock, in 1715.

Just before the end of the previous century, he had been engaged in shipping Liverpool's pauper children to Virginia to be bound apprentices there. The plight of these poor wretches moved him so deeply that he put aside one tenth of his fortune and income to found Liverpool's first charity school, the Bluecoat School where: 'Children could be provided with meat, drink, clothes and lodging and where they could be kept under such discipline as with the Blessing of God might provide the desired effect'. Robert Styth one of the joint rectors of Liverpool was the first treasurer. On his death in 1714 Blundell wrote: 'When I came home and found he was dead, it gave me much concern for the school — I therefore determined to leave off the sea and undertake the school'. It is to Blundell that we owe the superb Queen Anne buildings in which the school was housed and which are now known as Bluecoat Chambers.

He and his sons and later on his grandsons, like many other Liverpool merchants engaged in the slave trade, were owners or part owners of many vessels including the privateers *Mulberry*,

44   Richard Blundell, 1793-1853 *(Major C.V.R. Blundell)*

Providence, Pemberton, Queen, North Carolina, and Sea Flower.
When Bryan died in 1756 he had given £3,500 to the school. He
was also instrumental in founding the Liverpool Infirmary and the
Warrington Academy as well as thirty-six alms houses in Liverpool.

His son Richard took over as treasurer of the school but he
died in 1760 when Jonathan succeeded him. Under Jonathan the
school prospered greatly and within three years of his assuming
the treasurership, the number of pupils had increased by eighty
to two hundred. He remained treasurer of the school until 1796,
when due to failing health, he retired to Blackleyhurst Hall at
Billinge. His portrait and those of his father, brother and son hang
in the Governor's room of the modern Bluecoat School at Waver-
tree.

To return to Blundells' colliery enterprise, we have seen that
Jonathan owned a half share in the partnership by 1776, but
whether he bought out the remaining partners before the agreement had run its full ten years from 1774, we do not know. However, in the Land Tax Returns for 1784, the firm is no longer
described as Warren and Co but as Blundell and Co. He continued
working Saltersford Orrell Four Feet and the little that remained
of the Five Feet until it became exhausted near the end of the
eighteenth century.

Fig 45 shows the rate at which Blundells developed their first
colliery. In 1783-4 there were four pitshafts at this site. This colliery must have been nearing exhaustion in the 1790s, for it was in
March of 1791 that Blundell and Son took out important leases
of coal under Robert Holt Leigh's estate, and indeed in that decade they leased a total of over 170 Cheshire acres of Orrell Four
Feet from R.H. Leigh, the Duke of Bridgewater and the Rev Thomas Holme. Previous to the 1791 leases, they had purchased 'coal
estates at Kitt Green' which adjoined Leigh's coal.

Christmas festivities were not allowed to interfere with business
and Henry Blundell, Jonathan's son, who now seemed to by running the collieries, wrote to R.H. Leigh:

> Dear Sir, We have lately bought some coals in the neighbourhood of
> Peter Catterall's Estate. If you can dispose of the coals to us in this
> person's estate, we shall be glad to treat with you for them. Wishing
> you the compliments of the Season, we remain, very respectfully,
>> Your most obedient servants
>> Jonathan Blundell and Son

Fifteen months later, Leigh's solicitor, William Clayton who
lived at The Larches, Wigan Lane, Wigan, sent him a bill for work

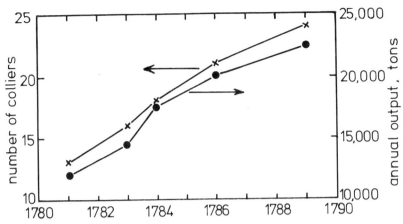

45 Number of colliers and probable annual output at Blundells' Saltersford (Orrell House) Colliery 1781-9

in connection with Hustler's release of 'the coal mines in Catteralls and Gaskells and leased by your father'. He also charged Leigh for drawing up an agreement between 'you and Mr Jonathan Blundell, concerning released mines'. There were further purchases of mineral estates five or six years later: '1795 Sundry persons for amount of coal estate purchased: £1,568 2s', '1796 To Peter Gaskell for coal estate purchased £118 19s 11d', '1796 To Richard Worthington for coal estate purchased £326 11s 0d'.

Blundells' first lease of March 1791 was for the Four Feet Seam under 34 Cheshire acres of the Edge Hall estate known at that time as Captain Birchall's. The rent was £500 per annum and the term was 20 years. On the same date, they also took out a lease of the Four Feet Mine under Catteralls land at Kitt Green and under the Gin Riding, the Higher Carr and the South East side of the Lower Carr under Peter Gaskells farm, 16 acres and 35 poles (Cheshire) in all. It was in this area that Blundell purchased coal estates four years later.

About the year 1794 Blundells leased the Orrell Four Feet Seam under the Duke of Bridgewater's estate in Winstanley at a rent of one sixth of the proceeds. This covered about 60 statute acres and adjoined the Edge Hall estate. The latter did not seem to be going very well for as late as January 1796 Henry Blundell wrote to R.H. Leigh saying that their agent, Mr Harvey, had seen Mr Robinson (presumably Leigh's agent):

who tells him he has no instructions from you to set out the land in Hedge [Edge] Hall Estate. We must beg the favour of you to appoint someone to do it as it is of *serious injury now every days delay* and you will much oblige Jonathan Blundell and Son.

In January 1799 the Rev Thomas Holme granted them a lease of the Four Feet Mine under his estate in Orrell which comprised 60 Cheshire acres. The boundary running from Dean Brook House opposite Abbey Lakes Hotel along Orrell Road up Spencers Lane and across the fields to the British Legion Club in Gathurst Lane, *Road* then along Gathurst Lane to Orrell House Farm boundary and back along Dean Wood to Abbey Lane. The term of the lease was twenty-one years and the certain rent £560 per annum; there was no footage rent. The colliery set up here was known as the Chain Colliery and it was operated by Henry Blundell and a new partner John Menzies who soon withdrew.

In those days — in this district at least — it was the common practice to lease the whole of the surface along with the minerals, and so it was with Blundells' leases. They farmed the land and felled timber in the woods when they required it, but the main reason for taking over the whole of the surface was to accomodate the large number of pit shafts and the many branch wagon-roads to them. The life of each coal drawing shaft was very short, generally two or three years at the most, and thus the branch wagon-roads were continually being re-routed to serve the pits winding coal at a particular time. Blundells sank at least fifty-nine pits in Orrell during the fifty or so years they worked collieries there,

Table 1. Annual Accounts of Blundell's Collieries at Orrell

Year	Output tons	Cost of working the collieries	Sales of house coal	Sales of Smiths Coal (Orrell 5ft)	Sales of slack	Sales of coke	Sales of cannel
		£	£	£	£	£	£
1788	18,250	3,651	9,737		8	75	
1789	22,320	4,464	10,765	170	49	43	
1790	27,175	5,436	14,083	355	93	89	
1791	38,840	7,485	15,152	664	93	99	474
1792	55,060	10,109	14,107	799	39	137	540
1793	46,490	8,185	17,716	84	98	45	637
1794	34,120	6,017	13,085		288	25	658
1795	37,770	6,740	12,705		495	49	912
1796	38,300	7,499	12,449		994	36	1,345
1797	35,205	7,042	12,768		799		908
1798	37,845	7,569	16,778		534		1,319
1799	42,480	8,496	19,993		645		900
1800	48,120	9,625	27,308		1,112		1,043

which means that on average they sank a new pit shaft every ten months. This was the practice in the district and as late as 1842 John Daglish, agent at Martha Ann German's Pemberton Colliery, stated that, rather than have the drawing roads more than 300yd with the consequent expense involved in paying for long drawing they would prefer to sink new shafts.

The output, which according to the number of colliers employed was around 12,000 tons in 1780, had doubled by 1790 and all this was from the Saltersford or Orrell House Pits. During the 1790s and the early part of the nineteenth century, the output was between 40,000 and 50,000 tons per annum and probably reached its peak during the first two decades of the nineteenth century. The table below gives some figures showing the progress of the business from 1788 to 1800. The table shows regular profits up to 1793 when there was a terrific loss for those days of £5,151. This was probably partly a consequence of the general upheaval caused by the outbreak of war with France at the beginning of 1793, but there was a financial crisis that year which hit Liverpool particularly hard. A high level of speculation in foreign goods in 1792, followed by a drop in commodity prices and coupled with uncertainty over the political situation led to lack of confidence and restriction of credit. A number of firms went

Table 1. (continued)

Cartage	Provision for horses etc.	Repair and hire of flats	River & canal clerks' & porters' wages etc.	Profit	Loss
£	£	£	£	£	£
320		781	2,790	2,040	
574		1,464	3,105	1,530	
1,356	693	1,727	4,071	1,263	
1,070	1,087	2,115	3,347	949	
1,539	908	2,325	4,431		5,151
1,045	1,020	2,081	4,173	1,057	
658	1,351	1,313	3,494	623	
1,033	849	1,492	3,036	201	
	903	1,476	4,492	341	
	975	1,415	4,572	950	
	1,133	1,617	5,316	2,390	
	1,782	1,873	5,999	2,902	
	3,402	3,638	9,195	3,577	

bankrupt, followed by a run on the banks, which swept away one
of Liverpool's most important banks.

Blundell and Leigh's other chief mineral lessee, Hustler, got into
difficulties with their coal trade and found it inconvenient to pay
Leigh the Certain Rent due. On the 10 August 1793, Henry Blundell wrote the following letter to Leigh who was staying at 'Mr
Forshaw's at Blackpool':

> Dear Sir, Money we apprehend is not scarce with you and we shall be
> obliged to you to let your £500 remain with us on interest some time
> longer, for really we are quite overloaded with our stocks of coals and
> cannel — would oblige us at this time, Jonathan Blundell and Son.

In further letters Blundell mentioned:

> the calamitous change that has taken place in our trade but such it is
> that last week we sold only 218 tons and do not take near so much
> money as pays the common wages independent of the great expense
> attending the opening of new works and we are therefore under the
> necessity of increasing our Capital to supply this want. This has deter-
> mined our J.B. to dispose of the Advowson of Halsall and has advertised
> it in the London papers to be sold, many applications have been made
> about it and we hope soon to dispose of it. It is valued at £11,050 but
> £10,000 is the price fixed.
> It is estimated in the neighbourhood of £1,300 per annum, but Mr
> Moore the present incumbent says we may warrant it a clear £1,000
> per annum.

Leigh was asked to forego the instalments due under the contract
until the trade recovered itself particularly as he was overpaid for
the quantity of coals already got. Blundell repeated that 'we have
not got by five acres what we have already paid you for, which
is not the case with your other Tenants, by acres on the other
hand'. He also stated that they had £937 river dues to pay 'this
month'. In the event Leigh agreed to accomodate them and they
did not find it necessary to sell the advowson of Halsall which
remains vested in Jonathan's descendants to this day.

As we have seen, Blundell, Earle, Warren and Birch had entered
into an agreement to purchase 38,500 scores of baskets of cannel
from the Ince Cannel Pits. After Blundell and his son Henry had
taken over the business they continued to purchase the cannel until
1791 when they took out a lease of the cannel pits at Ince on the
estate of R.H. Leigh and worked the mines themselves. For this
reason the accounts, from whence the figures in the table are extracted, include sales of cannel.

It is interesting to note that two-thirds to three-quarters of the
cannel produced at the cannel pits was sold at the works or in
Wigan, whereas the reverse was the case with the Orrell coals. Be-

tween 1788 and 1796 from 2 per cent to 7 per cent of the output was sold at the collieries. From 1796 to 1800 however, all the coal was sent down the canal to Liverpool. During a period of much industrial unrest 1792 was the only year in which the collieries showed a loss — albeit a large one — and Henry Blundell was much concerned about this, for, as well as being a colliery owner, he was also Mayor of Liverpool in 1791 and again in 1793. He was also concerned with the threat of William Roscoe MP for Liverpool and the other abolitionists, to put a stop to the slave trade and he led a deputation of those interested in the continuation of the trade to see the Duke of Clarence and obtain his support. In 1795 it was said that one fourth of the ships belonging to the Port of Liverpool were employed in the African trade and the port had three sevenths of the African trade of all Europe. A great outlet had been given to those in the slave trade by the British victory over the French in the West Indies. Lt Col Bryan Blundell, Henry's brother, had distinguished himself in the attack on Gaudaloupe and a 'Grand Banquet' was given by Henry in his honour and in his capacity as mayor. Bryan lies buried in the North Aisle of Exeter Cathedral where there is a monument to him.

A list of the 'Company of Merchants trading to Africa', includes Henry Blundell along with many friends and relations — the Earles, Crosbies, Gildarts, Bensons, Leighs, Branckers, Clarkes, Cases. During the Napoleonic invasion scare, Blundell raised a company of pioneers at the collieries to serve with the Liverpool Volunteers in which he was a lieutenant colonel. His landlord R.H. Leigh was a captain in the 1st Royal Lancashire Regiment of Militia at Wigan in 1799.

In 1769 Jonathan had built Larkhill, a large mansion in West Derby. It had a large five-windowed central block with a pedimented roof, a low colonnade in front and flanking wings, but fifteen years later he sold it to Heywoods, the family's bankers, and went to live in a large house which he had built at Leeds Street off Old Hall Street on the ground floor of which he opened his first coal office. Living with him in this house were his two brothers Bryan and the Rev Thomas Blundell (who later became Rector of Halsall) and his son Jonathan. Jonathan Junior died intestate in 1800 and in the form of oath administered to his widow when she claimed his estate he is described as 'Merchant of the Island of Jamaica'.

Soon after 1800 Henry Blundell was living at Summervale, Deysbrook, near Croxteth, known later on as Deysbrook House, and this was the family residence until the death of Col Henry B.H. Blundell in 1906.

For eighty years and during the whole of the Orrell Collieries period, Blundells' head office was at Canal Basin off Old Hall Street, Liverpool.

In 1802 Henry had inherited an estate and colliery at Blackrod on the north side of Wigan, from John Hollinshead, his father's colleague on the canal committee. Under the terms of the will he had to take the name and arms of Hollinshead and thenceforward he was known as Henry Blundell Hollinshead. Up to 1806 a firm known as Blundell and Hollinshead held a licence for plying packet boats on the canal between Liverpool and Wigan, but whether the Hollinshead was Henry or his benefactor is not clear.

During the life of their Orrell Collieries, Blundells also worked Ince Cannel Works, Blackrod Colliery and Pemberton Colliery, which Henry had started to develop in about 1815. By 1830 the pits at Orrell were finished, John Ashurst, 'underlooker to Mr Blundell' told a Court of Enquiry in 1872 that 'all the pillars were worked out at Blundells collieries forty five years before'. William Bryham, Mining Engineer, stated at the same enquiry that his father, also a mining engineer, had made plans of Blundells' colliery workings in 1810 and 1811 and he confirmed that it was forty-four to forty-five years since he rememberd the pits at Edge Hall being worked. Squire Meyrick Bankes in a survey of his estate in 1834 noted that there were many disused pit brows on what was Holme's Orrell estate and the site of Blundells' Chain Colliery which needed clearing away so that the land could be restored.

Although Blundells worked Amberswood, Mesnes and Chorley collieries after Orrell finished, their greatest venture was the Pemberton Colliery which although not in the Orrell belt, was just on the east side of the Tinker Hole Fault and indeed the last piece of coal worked at the Summersales Pit in the 1960s was a reserved area of Orrell Four Feet Seam under the pleasure grounds of Winstanley Hall in our Orrell Belt.

Blundells greatest enterprise as it appeared near the end of the nineteenth century was described thus:

Jonathan Blundell & Son, Colliery Proprietors, Borough Buildings, Rumford Street, Liverpool. — The Business under consideration represents one of the greatest industrial enterprises in the North, and the Blundell family, by whom it is controlled, has long been identified with the development of the natural resources of Lancashire. The present Proprietor is the great grandson of the founder, and succeeded, on the death of his father in 1853, to the great mineral estate whence the coal in which the firm trade so extensively is derived. The importance of that coalfield will be appreciated when it is stated that the output of the firm's pits represents about half a million tons per annum, and that the industry carried on affords employment to nearly two thousand hands. Mr Blundell the present owner, was formerly a colonel, in the Grenadier Guards, and is now member of Parliament for the Ince division of Lancashire. His brother is a general in the Indian army. Mr Blundell married the late Hon Miss Beatrice Byng, who was one of the Queen's Maids of Honour, and a descendant of the historic Admiral Byng. Her father, also, was an admiral. The Blundell family have always taken a great interest in the welfare of the district with which they are identified, and it is to Bryan Blundell Liverpool owes that splendid institution the Bluecoat Hospital, he being one of the principle founders in .1702, and was appointed second secretary in 1714. Other members of the family have actively participated in affairs of civic import and have served as Mayors, Aldermen and Town Councillors. The head offices of the firm in Liverpool are extensive, and in connection with them, a large staff is employed, under the direction of the Manager, Mr James Pickering.

A feature of the business is the supply direct to consumers by a firm who are themselves colliery proprietors. The public are thus offered exceptional advantages, which they have not been slow to appreciate, superior household coal being delivered at minimum prices.

The supplies include Orrell coals, classified as firsts, seconds, cobbles and nuts; Pemberton coal, Wigan coal, King coal, and slack. The firm make a speciality of the new class of coal designated 'cobbles', which considering their quality, are the cheapest coals in the market.

A feature of the retail trade is the delivery of coal in bags — a system which limits the breakage of coal in delivery and prevents dirt and annoyance. The advantages of this system only entails an extra charge of 1s per ton, including, in ordinary cases, the cost of storage. For the convenience of customers throughout the district, there are branch depots in various localities on both sides of the Mersey. The principle of direct dealing which the great colliery firm of Jonathan Blundell and Son has so long adopted is a modern development which has proved a boon to the public, and the success which has attended their enterprise has fully justified it. Moreover, under such a system the perfection of organisation and prompt deliveries as well as the most moderate prices are secured.

4.2 THE HOLME-BANKES COLLIERIES AT WINSTANLEY AND ORRELL

These collieries differed from all the others in the Orrell coalfield in that they were owned and worked by local landowners, as distinct from the other and generally speaking, larger collieries, which were worked by Liverpool and Bradford capitalists.

Winstanley Collieries

The Winstanley collieries in particular have a record of continuous production which is hard to beat. It is probably true to say that they have been worked continuously from at least the time of Elizabeth I right up to the present day. The licenced mine,

Windy Arbour Colliery, now represents Winstanley collieries, the pit shaft there having been sunk by Meyrick Bankes in 1843. The earliest date for coal mining in Winstanley so far discovered is 1507, two years before the death of Henry VII. Thomas Winstanley who died in 1562 made provision in his will for part of the profits of the Winstanley Colliery to be used for the benefit of his children and in 1595 when James Bankes bought the estate, the list of tenants included 'William Barton of the Coalpits'.

However, to return to our period, the colliery, which was valued at £200 in 1754, was doing quite well according to some interesting accounts which have survived. The accounts for 1766, for instance, show that the Moorhey Pit produced 33-73 tons per week with a face output of 44-60cwt per manshift, and the Lime Piece Pit produced 24-90 tons per week with a face output of 40-60cwt per manshift. It is interesting to compare these figures with those of 1947, the first year of nationalisation, when the face output averaged 58.4cwt per manshift. The two pits produced weekly profits of £4 16s (£4.80) to £15 14s (£15.70) in 1766, but up to £3 13s (£3.65) a week had to be deducted from this for the development costs of two other pits, sinking a pit, driving a sough etc.

Payment by scores instead of loads was introduced in February 1766, the Winstanley load at that time being nine baskets. The colliers seem to have been allowed to work the pit once a year for a whole week, without any payment of wages, for the production of their own 'fire coal', or concessionary coal as it is now called. This happened around Michaelmas, when they were hired or rehired. At the Moorhey Pit, seven colliers got 7 tons 10cwt each and a like amount is shown as being 'spent at the hiring'. The six colliers at the Lime Piece Pit got the same amount each but only 6 tons was spent at the hiring. At the Tuson Lane and Salterley Pits six men were engaged on opening out and development work and they also got and received 7½ tons each with 6 tons again being spent at the hiring. This fire coal was worth almost three weeks' wages to the collier, which is very similar to the value of the concessionary coal received by the modern miner. Apart from this, 2s 6d (12½p) was paid to each man when he was hired and for Good Friday, which was a holiday, the twenty-three men and lads received 3d each.

'Hauming the hack' recorded as 'helving the hack' at Halliwell's colliery, was another excuse for a celebration, £2 8s (£2.40) being spent on meat and drink at the Moorhey and Lime Piece pits and £1 12s 7d (£1.63) at the Salterley and Tuson Lane pits. 'Hack' is an old name for pick, the shaft or helve of which was still referred to as a 'pick haum' by the older miners at Pemberton Colliery forty years ago.

We have seen the comparison between the output per manshift of the colliers or getters at Winstanley Colliery in 1766 and that of the NCB in 1947. The overall output per manshift for the week that twenty-three men and lads are recorded as being on the books, (owing to having received 3d for Good Friday) comes to 22.6cwt. This is assuming that all of them worked five days. The overall figure for Great Britain for the year 1947 — the first year of nationalisation — was 21.5cwt. No doubt the shift worked in 1766 at Winstanley would be longer than the 7¼ hours worked in 1947.

At this time, the annual output of the Winstanley pits was between 3,500 and 5,000 tons, although by 1799 sales and presumably raisings had risen to 8,030 tons.

The pattern of work probably did not alter much until the pits in the old Winstanley Park area eventually became exhausted early in the 1840s. By that time four new and much deeper pits had been sunk by Meyrick Bankes in a virgin area of coal east of the Croppers House Fault.

Holme's Orrell and UpHolland Collieries

Anne Bankes of Winstanley who married Hugh Holme of Holland House in 1731 was the sole heiress of her father, brothers and nephew. Their eldest son Thomas was William Bankes's cousin and he inherited the Winstanley estate on the latter's death in 1800. Thomas himself died in 1803 and was succeeded by his son Meyrick who, under the terms of William Bankes's will, changed his name to Bankes. Thus the Orrell and UpHolland Collieries of the Holme family and those at Winstanley belonging to the Bankes family came under the same ownership in 1800.

Holme's Orrell Colliery, like that of Winstanley, had been extensively worked long before our period. Edward Holme's collieries had progressed sufficiently to warrant the installation of a water-wheel driven pumping engine at his colliery near Dean Wood in 1710.

Edward died shortly after this and his widow, Martha, leased the colliery for a term of fifteen years to James Leyland of Ormskirk and James Corless, a joiner, of UpHolland. Two pits were already down to the coal, the Engine Pit and the Whimsey Pit, but they had liberty to sink and sough pits in any part of Martha Holme's land in Orrell. They were to pay a yearly rent of £35, but if they discontinued working the coal before the expiration of the term, a penalty of £50 per annum was to be paid. Leyland and Corless were to have the use of the pumping engine and any other colliery tackle and equipment in Martha Holme's possession.

46 William Bankes 1709-55/6
    (Mrs J.H.M. Bankes)

47 William Bankes, 1751-1800
    (Mrs J.H.M. Bankes)

She had also to provide winding ropes for the Engine and Whimsey Pits and to make up the pump 'stocks' or pipes to 40yd in length. These no doubt would be of elm or some similar wood, the stipulated length seeming to indicate that the Engine Pit was 40yd deep. In addition to the above, Martha had to provide all the timber necessary for the timbering of the coalpit. The lessees on their part had to provide her with coal for domestic use and for her kilns and they had to leave the pumping engine in good repair on the termination of the lease.

At the beginning of our period on 26 November 1744, William Fairclough, Mrs Holme's banksman, hired eight men to work at her coalpits until the following Michaelmas, ie less than a twelve month's bond. Thomas Gee was to sink the Little Pit at a price of 4s (20p) per yard, and Thomas Howard and Joseph Lancaster were to sink the 'New Pitt in the meadow by Brownlow's House', at a rate of 7s (35p) per yard. Each man received 12d (5p) 'in earnest'. Some interesting instructions for development work are given:

> The level is drove 30 yards and is to be driven further 20 yards. A pit to be sunk at the end of the said level which will be in the depth 29.
>
> A pit to be sunk by the milln and that pit to be worked from in the coal Each Way.

Won to go under the Milln wheell to loose an auger hole bord' down under the said wheele

The other to go towards the little pitt into the Hollows to make a water course that was to draw (drain) the work to the level of the sleam ditch.

Which is supposed will lay the top of the falt dry that lyeth under Brownlows house.

The level under Brownlows house to be drove first, and the pit to be sunk during the time the levels are in driving by the Milln. Tho. Gee says this level is not necessary to be drove, Nor the pitt loosed nor has any been loosed in the works only one.

A later record shows that five colliers were hired to work in these pits and they were to be paid 9d (4p) a score:

And to drive two ends from the water lane, the right hand drift to go 25 yards and the left hand drift to go 40 yards at 12d a score (2d paid in earnest for drifts'. And if they can't possibly draw the coal upon sledges Mrs Holmes to find five wheelbarrows, and 12 pence apiece

48 Meyrick Bankes II eldest son of Meyrick Bankes I and grandson of Rev Thomas Holme of Holland House, receiving tenants at Winstanley Hall about 1846. William Starkey, who is at the head of Pony Dick, changed the name of the 'Horse and Jockey' public house to 'The Favourite Pony Dick' when he became landlord there later. *(Mrs J.H.M. Bankes)*

49 Holland House, where the Holme family lived

given to each of them in earnest for each bargain as witness their hands,

In presence of
John Shirley,
Richd Topping.

Markes of
Peter Frodsham
Thomas Howarth
Joseph Lancaster
Richard Culshaw
John Amory.

N.B. 2/6 given for removing slack etc. falling in the drifts.

Apparently if any of the men took on bargain or yard work such as sinking, channelling, or driving a road 'on end' the others were to join him, or if they did not like the price he had agreed to for the work, they were to cast lots to decide who should join him. During most of the time the number of colliers varied between four and eight, and the output varied accordingly.

Although in 1748 a new sough had been driven, the extension of the workings to the dip made it necessary in 1773-4 to erect a steam pumping engine and pumps at the deepest pit: 'by powder nails candles etc. on ye engine account £31 17s 10d'. Another item for materials reads 'ye engine being finished £5 19s 6d'. There are regular amounts shown in the accounts after this for coal supplied for the engine boiler fire. This engine was offered to Blundell in his lease of the Four Feet Mine under the Holmes estate and no doubt he took it over and adapted it to suit the greater depth of the pit.

During the decade 1770-9 output varied between 1,968 and 5,324 tons per annum, the average being 4,068 tons per annum. Again during the following decade 1780-9 the figures are 2,560 to 4,623 tons per annum, with an average of 3,600 tons per annum. During the next fifteen year period the output averaged about 5,900.

Towards the end of the colliery's life the Drynole Pit seems to have been the only winding pit. This pit raised 2,471 tons in 1817 and 2,046 tons in 1818; 3,900 baskets of oven coke were sold in 1817 but only 900 in 1818, although coke was burned every week. The number of colliers from the beginning of 1817 up to 5 March of that year was four and a learner. After getting rid of the learner, the number of colliers dropped to three on 26 April 1817 and varied between three and two up to the end of 1818.

The ratio of profits to expenditure was quite fantastic compared with that of a modern mine. In 1817 the total cost for getting, drawing, yard work, winding, drawing off props, burning coke, way candles, underground and surface day wages for men boys and girls, coal for the smithy and cabin fires, workmen's concessionary coal and odd items like ale for the workmen at Christmas amounted to £591 8s 11½d (£591.45). The value of the coal raised and the coke burned was £1,866 4s 7d (£1,866.23) leaving a profit of £1,264 7s 7½d (£1,264.38). The figures for 1818 were: cost of working the colliery £408 8s 1½d (£408.40), value of coal and coke produced £1,382 16s 5d (£1,381.82), profit £972 8s 3½d (£972.41).

No pit shafts were sunk nor were any soughs driven during these two years and in any case the pits were only shallow and not costly to sink. A new pit sunk at this colliery in 1814 cost only £53 2s 4d. Also with regard to drainage, as Henry Blundell was working the Orrell Four Feet Seam below the Holme-Bankes colliery, the water from the latter pits was pumped by Blundells' engines.

4.3 THE BERRY - GERMAN - CLARKE CONCERN

In 1777 the Post House estate in Orrell belonged to William Berry who advertised it for sale:

Wherein is a valuable coal mine the vein or bed of which by a late boring has been found to be 4ft 3ins thick, to lie very true, of an excellent quality and is presumed from the different borings to run through the whole estate; and which may be worked to singular advantage owing to the vicinity of the River Douglas at Gathurst Bridge, thereby commanding a foreign as well as a home sale.

In 1780 Berry applied for leave to build a wagon road from his colliery to the new cut to Wigan. A year or two later, the colliery was referred to as 'the Great Colliery of Berrys' which was said 'to make of profit no more than 3½d per ton'.

A third share in the estate and colliery was advertised for sale
in April 1781. The advertisement stated that there were 'three pits
down and now at work' in a seam of coal four feet thick

> the coals all laid dry and now in getting by a very large and compleat
> Fire Engine are known to be the best coals for all uses in this County;
> there may be got large quantities of coals every year for fifty or sixty
> years: with a good and commodious railed or plank road, that coals
> may be got at an easy expence to the Leeds Canal; the road made of
> new oak timber. Good sale for coal to Liverpool, Preston, Lancaster
> and several ports of the Fild country, likewise a very good country
> sale.

Prospective purchasers were to apply to Thomas Sherratt at the
colliery. A year later the whole estate was advertised: 'To be let
by the Trustees of Mr William Berry for a term of years'. It was
stated that: 'The coals are drawed by a very complete Fire Engine'
which on the face of it would seem to refer to a winding engine
but it is more likely to mean the pumping engine.

There were eight 'waggons' for carrying the coal to the River
Douglas and the Leeds and Liverpool Canal. The coals were described as 'good house coals and for smithy firing and the slack
made the best cinders [coke] or charcoal for maltsters, millers and
founders'. There were carpenters' and blacksmiths' shops at the
colliery. No prospective lessee came forward and the trustees continued to work the colliery.

Orrell, April 23d, 1781.

To be SOLD or LET,

ONE Third, or One Half, of all that ESTATE and
COAL-MINE, lying in *Orrell*, near *Wigan*, commonly called *Poft-Houfe Eftate*, containing 52 Acres (8 Yards
to the Pole or Perch) of Land, and Coals all laid dry, and
now in getting by a very large and compleat Fire-Engine ; are
known to be the beft Coals for all Ufes in this County ; there
may be got large Quantities of Coals every Year, for 50 or 60
Years : With a good and commodious Rail'd or Plank Road,
that Coals may be got down at any eafy Expence to the *Leeds
Canal*, the Road made of new Oak Timber. Good Sale for
Coals to *Liverpool, Prefton, Lancafter*, and feveral Parts of the
Field County. Likewife a very good Country Sale.

Further Particulars may be had by applying to *Tho. Sherratt*,
at the above Colliery, from the above Date till the 25th of
May next.

N. B. There are three *Pits* down, and now at Work to the
above Vein, which is four Feet of clear Coal.

50   Advertisement for the sale of a colliery and fire engine at Orrell in 1781

51 Orrell Mount, built by John Clarke

William Ingold, formerly Blundells' agent and Robert Worthington of Liverpool, coal merchant, had agreed to sell the coal on commission for 'William Clarke and others, Trustees of the estate of William Berry & Co', but things went wrong and 'the said Ingold stands justly and truly indebted in a very considerable sum of money had and received by him from the said partnership concern and applied to his own private use'. Ingold personally had to give Clarke and the other trustees a bond for payment of £900 in annual instalments of £225, plus interest, up to 1792.

The partnership owed the trustees of William Berry & Co £4,181 9s 7¾d (£4,181.48) and the first dividend of 5s (25p) in the pound amounting to £1,045 7s 5d (£1,045.37) was paid in January 1790.

William Clarke's father, William, had established Liverpool's first bank in 1774 and in 1777 he had taken his two sons William, who was then 24, and John, 21, into partnership with him. The bank was on the corner of Dale Street and Castle Street.

Some idea of the output of Berry's colliery can be gained from a note attached to a letter dated January 1789 which states that: 'Mr Berry's coaliery which lies about one and a half miles further [from Liverpool] than that of Dean Wood pays £12 per day tonnage at 2s 6d a ton but as to go through two locks'. £12 a day at 2s 6d (12½p) per ton gives a daily shipment down the canal of 160 tons. Taking 280 working days in the year this is equal to 44,800 tons annually.

It was at this time that John Clarke became a partner in a colliery at Gathurst. By an indenture of the 13 June 1789 Thomas Porter, late of Ackhurst, but then of Souldern in Oxfordshire leased to John Clarke of Liverpool, banker, William Roscoe of Liverpool, gent, William German of Orrell, coalmaster, and Charles Porter of Ackhurst, coalmaster 'all that mine, delph and vein of coal called the Four Feet or deep mine' under the Gathurst and Ackhurst estates. The lease was for a term of 21 years. They were to pay a yearly rent of £50 plus £10 per acre above that for the Gathurst estate and £380 per Cheshire acre of the demised coal seam.

The partnership agreement dated 1st January 1790 stipulated that the firm would be known as Chas Porter & Co:

> The capital requisite for carrying on the business shall be advanced by the said parties hereto in the shares and proportions following:- i.e. John Clarke two fifths, William Roscoe one fifth, William German one fifth and Charles Porter one fifth.

They were to receive profits and bear losses in the same proportions and meet at least four times a year. A book was to be kept in Liverpool with the conditions of the agreement, etc in it. Books of account were to be properly kept and no bills were to be written without the consent of two partners in writing.

However, the concern did not run smoothly at first and on 17 February 1791, Roscoe wrote the following letter to Porter:

> Sir,
> Although it is extremely inconvenient to enter into a discussion of our partnership concerns by letter, yet as in the last you favoured me with, I find you are under some mistakes I should not think I was acting either a friendly or a proper part if I did not use my endeavours to remove them.
>
> It cannot be unknown to you that when I took a share in the colliery my dependence with respect to the management was placed *solely on Mr German* who I know to be an experienced collier. I consider now however that your vicinity to the works, and the leisure time you have (for I did not understand you was engaged in any business) might be advantageous to the Concern and that you would probably choose to take upon you the superintendance of the accounts at a reasonable Salary.
>
> I confess I never perfectly understood how *the whole management* came to devolve on you; and I never had an idea at the time the agreement was made that this was to be the case. Unwilling however to give offence to a person for whom I entertained respect, and of whose integrity I had a good opinion, I did not oppose it; choosing rather to judge by the event though at some risque of loss, than to propose any measure that might give offence. Whether I had patience or not you will judge, when you consider, that although you began with *a pit ready sunk* yet at the end of the first year when an acre of coals was to be paid for not half an acre was gotten and that instead of any prospect of improvement, the whole work seemed to be nearly at a stand. And here I must beg you will do me the favour to make a distinction in what I have said on this subject in which you seem to apprehend I have contradicted myself. I believe I have both in my letters and in conversation told you I was convinced *you had used your best endeavours* and done all that lay in your powers to promote the interest of the Concern and in my last I have said that if we are to have any profit it must be *by better management* than formerly or to that effect. Now it always was and still is my opinion that you exerted yourself to the utmost to get the

concern in order but it was also equally evident that your exertions *totally failed* of success, and that if we had proceeded in the same way nothing but a heavy loss was to be expected. To what circumstances this was owing, I cannot pretend to say. You accuse Mr German of witholding Men and being partial to Berrys Colliery but between ourselves though, I have a good opinion of Mr German, I scarcely can think it probable he would lean towards Berrys work, *in which he has no concern* rather than to the Gathurst in which he has one fifth. Probably the reasons are to be sought for in the difficult nature of such an undertaking, and in too great a degree of economy in the outset, by which a large undertaking may be said to be starved before it is born. Whatever the reasons may be I am told the delay has cost the concern upwards of £500; and that a business which it was hoped would make such instant returns as almost to prevent the necessity of an advance will now require a considerable Capital. On our last meeting at Orrell I could not avoid thinking you saw the concern was going to decay and I apprehend the proposal of Mr German was no less agreeable to you than to myself. To me I own it was agreeable because I saw it was neither *in your power* nor I believe in that of *any other Man* in the Kingdom except Mr German to work the mine with sufficient effect to fulfil our contract and here I cannot help opposing an opinion you entertain that our mine is sacrificed to Berrys. If this were really the case, I must either be *very dull sighted* or very liberal in my opinions to submit to such an abuse. But I am convinced that this is by no means the case and I hope and have reason to believe that a little time will satisfy you that this charge is not well founded.

With respect to your salary I shall by no means oppose *any allowance* which the other partners may think reasonable. On enquiry respecting Mr German I find he had only £50 *per annum* for the first two or three years, without *House, Horse or Cow*. It shall not however be a trifling business of this nature that shall give rise to any disagreement so far as I can help it.

I was not consulted any more than yourself respecting the engaging a clerk and I assure you it would have given me pleasure if you would have continued to superintend the Accounts but this you positively refused at our last meeting except in such a manner as would not suit the interests of the concern. The measure was therefore unavoidable, for we have *all of us* too much at stake to be trifled with.

I should be glad if anything I have said or could say would satisfy you as to the present conduct of the Colliery and prevent a repetition of those disagreements that have rendered our meetings so uncomfortable but after the receipt of your last letters, I despair of it. It is some comfort however that the mines begin to be worked with effect, and that we are now in a fair way of fulfilling our contract for the present year. In due time I hope we shall be able to bring matters to a conclusion; when, if we both live we may perhaps meet on better terms. As I assure you, I shall always be happy in showing a proper sence of your civilities and in convincing you that notwithstanding the doubts you seem to entertain, I am very sincerely, Your Friend and Servant

William Roscoe

Poor Mr Porter! His two beautiful daughters who had been expensively educated at York, caused him much heartache. The elder

52   William Roscoe MP, 1753-1831, partner in Orrell Collieries
(Walker Art Gallery, Liverpool)

one eloped to Gretna with a poor clerk and the younger one married a journeyman butcher from Wigan. Worry over his daughters brought about declining health and finally death in 1808.

An interesting point here is that German had from 1784 been mentioned in the Land Tax Returns as tenant of Berry's Colliery but it is obvious from Roscoe's letter that he was only the agent or manager with no financial interest in it.

In September 1790 John Clarke, his brother William and William German took out a lease from Francis, 3rd Duke of Bridgewater of the 'Lower or Four Feet Mine' in 6½ Cheshire acres of his estate and under what is now Loch Street, Macdonald Street and Bradshaw Street on the north side of Orrell Road at Lamberhead Green. They obviously thought the prospects were good and it was not long before they had their eyes on the great area of virgin Orrell Four Feet under part of the Winstanley estate. The upper seam had been worked over an extensive area for many generations by the Bankes family and by this time it was realised that the Four Feet Seam could be relied upon to make an appearance 62-4yds below the Five Feet.

During the preliminary negotiations between William Bankes and Clarke and German the former stated that according to his calculations one Cheshire acre of the Orrell Four Feet Seam contained

15,000 tons. German asserted that these calculations were wrong and that such a quantity never was produced but 7,000 tons per acre was nearer the mark. The seam varied in thickness in the area under negotiation between 3ft 6in and 3ft 9in and taking what became the customary figure of 3,200 tons per foot thick, one acre would contain between 11,200 and 12,000 tons. Bankes was talking about the amount of coal contained in an acre, whereas German was insisting on production figures and these would not be more than 80-90 per cent of the gross, allowing for shaft-pillars, parts of pillars and stumps abandoned when roof weights came on, etc and pillars left to support water-ways. Therefore the tonnage produced per acre would probably be between 8,960 and 10,800 tons. An interesting point which all three agreed on was that the whole expense of getting 7,000 tons would be about or above £300. Allowing it to be £350 for 7,000 tons this is only 1s (5p) per ton which, with the selling price of coal about 6-7s (30-35p) per ton, would allow for quite fantastic profits, even taking into account the heavy expense for fire engines, sinking the new pits, rents and royalties etc. In fact during the period 1810-16 the colliery did make a clear profit of 4s (20p) per ton.

The lease dated 1 May 1792 for a term of 20 years was for 'all that one Mine Delf, Bed, or Vein of coal commonly called or known by the name of the Four Feet or Lower Mine' under 77 Cheshire acres, 3 roods, 23 perches of land starting at Smithy Brook in the Pingot and extending westwards on both sides of Hall Lane (or Nicholsons Lane as it was known locally) with its southern boundary running through the New Covert and the Gardens Wood in Winstanley Park to a point near the UpHolland Lodges in Winstanley Road on the south side of UpHolland Grammar School. The western boundary was Winstanley Road (Old Road) down to Orrell brick yard. From here it meandered back to the Pingot along the boundary of what was then the Duke of Bridgewater's estate in Winstanley.

There was a provision to demise and lease for thirty years, from the expiry of the first lease in 1812, the remainder of the Four Feet Mine under William Bankes's land lying on the north-west side of the Tinker Hole Fault. Some other provisions of the lease were as follows:

Coal had to be left for support under all dwelling houses, barns, stables, etc. Working had to stop 10yd from any building.

They were at liberty to construct wagon-roads or roads to convey it away by tunnels to any point between Rylands Mill Bridge and Captain Birchall's in Orrell (Edge Hall). They were not to use any of the highways or other lanes or roads in Winstanley for this purpose.

They were to have the use of the sough driven in the 1760s, which

drained the Five Feet Mine from a point under the Salterley Fields, ie
the area near the Makerfield Water Board's disused pumping pit known
as Nicholson's Pit, to the brook at Rylands Mill near Pony Dick and if
required they could drive soughs or tunnels in this seam which were
not to exceed 4yd in width or 5ft when driven under a building.

They were allowed to get stone sand and gravel for colliery use and
they could use the existing stone quarry in little Gathurst at the north
end of Summersales which up to recent years was known as Sarah
Plumbe's Delf.

The lessees were at liberty to use any existing shafts or soughs and surface streams, but not to impede the working of Ryland's and Smithy
Brook Mills which were both water corn-mills.

In certain parts of the Winstanley demesnes and woods no shafts, engines, buildings, or brick burning were allowed.

At the request of William Bankes in writing they were, by means of
the fire engine to be erected and soughs and water courses to be driven
to 'free and clear from water all the upper or Five Feet Mine of coal
in the lands of the said William Bankes in Winstanley'. Bankes was to
make reasonable compensation and satisfaction to Clarke & Co for this.

An important condition of the lease was that the lessees had to drive a
drift or water course in the seam from the proposed Engine Pit towards the crop to a point between Snuffgate Lane and the lane leading
to what was then George Gaskell's farm. This point would be somewhere near the Orrell end of Up Holland Grammar School grounds in
Winstanley Road.

The drift or water course was to be 'at least four feet but not to exceed
five feet wide with pillars or ranges of coal on each side thereof of
4 yards thick and 6 yards length each'. It was described later as being
arched with brickwork.

The lessors' agents were to have power to descend any of the Clarke
and Co's pits to see that the mine was being 'fairly duly and properly
and in a regular and collier-like and skilful manner wrought', and also
to 'measure and dial the said premises'.

The Royalty fixed was £200 per Cheshire acre measured on the surface
with no allowance for faults, rolls or washouts, unless one sixteenth
of an acre of the coal was affected.

The scale of certain rents gave the lessees time to lay out and
develop the colliery properly and increased regularly from £50 in
1794 to £1,400 in 1811.

Whilst the Winstanley Colliery was being developed, the Clarke
brothers and Richard Fisher German, William German's son (the
father having died) had taken out a lease of the Four Feet Mine
under an area, part of which belonged to Robert Holt Leigh and
the remainder to William Bankes. The northern boundary was Orrell
Road, the western boundary was a line running directly south to
Captain's Clough Wood, the eastern boundary was Brook Lane and
the southern boundary, Smithy Brook in Captain's Clough Wood.
The lease stated that the western boundary was 'a line drawn from

the east corner of the Holy Post towards and by the steam engine of Jonathan Blundell and Son to the brook which divides Orrell and Winstanley'. Altogether the area comprised 38 acres, 2 roods, 18 perches of the Cheshire measure. The lease was for 21 years, the certain rent being £500 after the first year when it was £400 and the Royalty £260 per Cheshire acre for William Bankes's coal and £200 per Cheshire acre for R.H. Leigh's coal.

On the expiry of the first Winstanley lease in 1812 a new lease for thirty years was drawn up for what was known as the 'second lot' containing 100 Cheshire acres with a provision for a further extension of twenty years if all the coal had not then been got. Three arbitrators were appointed to decide on the amount of royalty. One was chosen by Meyrick Bankes who had succeeded William, one by John Clarke and the third by the other two arbitrators. They were William Robinson, engineer of UpHolland and manager of Hustler's collieries, William Holding, Clarke's agent, and John Haddock. The house where Holding lived is still known as Holding's House and stands next door to Orrell Police Station. Robinson lived at Ayrefield. The arbitrators fixed the certain rent at £1,000 per annum with a royalty per Cheshire acre of £256. Any remaining coal at the end of the term was to be worked by Clarke at the rate of three acres per year and this would give him an output of about 30,000 tons per year depending upon the percentage of extraction. As the shafts, wagon ways and buildings etc. became disused, the shafts were to be filled up, the pit banks and wagon ways levelled and the land restored to arable cultivation.

The first pits to be sunk were the Engine and Bye Pit. The Engine Pit, now capped with concrete, is on the north side of the main railway line from Wigan to Liverpool in the Pingot. The Bye Pit, also capped with concrete, is on the opposite side of the railway lines and actually inside the railway fence. The large pumping engine erected at the Engine Pit and the one subsequently erected at the Bye Pit are fully described in the chapter on pumping engines. (After the colliery finished in 1852 the Bye Pit was used for many years by the Lancashire and Yorkshire Railway Company in the days of steam as a pumping station for feeding the standpipe tanks that supplied the locos with water). Between the railway and Winstanley Park cricket field ten more pits were sunk during the first fifteen years of the lease and the same pattern was followed over the whole of the area leased, forty-two coal drawing pits being sunk altogether. Apart from the Engine Pit the shafts were numbered up to No 42 Pit which was sunk on the north side of Park Road not far from Longshaw Bottom. As usual the colliers themselves gave the pits names of their own. Apart from

the Engine and Bye Pits there were the Bridge, Boundary, Nicholson's, Bankes's and Lane pits between the Pingot and Winstanley
Road. The Lane Pit was on the edge of Winstanley Road on the
south side of Orrell YMCA club. Hulberts Farm Pit was situated
near the farm now known as Farrars by the side of UpHolland
Grammar School. Other shafts were Snuffgate Lane Pit near the
old estate club, Fairhouse Pit near Moss Wood, Moor Mill Pit at
the southern end of Orrell reservoirs, and in the fields going on to
Park Road, Volunteer Pit, Anakims Pit, Coachman's Pit and two
known as the Top Pits, to mention only a few.

At some time around 1815 the colliers in the Bridge Pit put
through to a large body of water in Blundells' workings on the
Duke of Bridgewater's estate. William Houghton one of these colliers who later on became the underlooker said 'we all had to run
for it, we had to fly to another pit for refuge lest we should be
drowned'. After the water burst in upon them, the two pumping
engines were worked to full capacity night and day for several
years until they got the dead water out.

Clarke & Co were extremely fortunate in obtaining the services
of Robert Daglish as their manager about the year 1810-11. Daglish and his son became quite eminent in engineering circles. An
obituary notice in the annual report of the Institution of Civil
Engineers for 1866-7 stated

> Robert Daglish born 21st Dec. 1779. Settled in Wigan in 1804 as en-
> gineer to Lord Balcarres and managed Haigh Foundry and Brock Mill
> Forge. He there constructed the Arley Engine and many other pump-
> ing, winding and blast engines which were celebrated in their day as
> improved and efficient machines. After some years experience of these
> works Mr. Daglish took the management of the Orrell Collieries near
> Wigan and whilst there he constructed the railway in connection with
> it. He at once appreciated and applied to this railway, the then novel
> invention of the locomotive steam engine of Mr. John Blenkinsop of
> Leeds in which the power was applied by a large cog wheel working
> in a rack laid down beside the ordinary rail. By arrangement with the
> patentee Mr. Daglish constructed a loco of this description in the year
> 1812 and started it on this railway in 1813. It was known as the "York-
> shire Horse" and was long looked upon with interest by all concerned
> with the advancement of engineering science. Under Mr. Daglish's man-
> agement, the Orrell Colliery became a most successful undertaking and
> Orrell coal in that district has become the equivalent of Wallsend in
> the north.

The total amount of coal available for working at the colliery
in the 177 Cheshire acres in lease and allowing for 80 per cent
extraction was 1,600,000 tons. Thus the average tonnage for each
of the forty-two shafts was 38,100 and 4.2 Cheshire acres was the
average area worked by each shaft. This is very nearly equal to

an area 202yd square. It will be seen from this that the life of each shaft was quite short, a matter of a very few years at the most.

Although the colliery was going well, calamity overtook the banking side of Clarke's business in 1816. A notice in the *Liverpool Mercury* for 26 January 1816 stated:

> We are extremely concerned to find that the house of Roscoe, Clarke and Roscoe bankers have been obliged to announce to the public a suspension of their payments and their determination to call a meeting for taking into consideration the measures to be adopted for the satisfactory liquidating of all demands upon them.

On 3 February 1816 a meeting of the creditors was held to investigate the balance sheet then produced. This showed that the debts owing by Roscoe, Clarke and Roscoe amounted to £314,626 and the debts owing to them £166,295, but bad debts reduced this figure to £115,903. Clarke's personal property was estimated at £135,278 and Roscoe's at £61,725. Clarke was then the sole owner of Orrell Colliery and Roscoe owned Dee Bank Colliery at Bagilt in Flintshire. Reports on these two concerns were submitted to the creditors:

> With respect to the Orrell Colliery belonging to Mr. Clarke, there were certain data on which to proceed. It had upon an average of 12 years produced a clear revenue after allowing for rent, expenses, repairs and wear and tear of the machinery, but not of interest upon the capital (because it belonged to Mr. Clarke) of £11,000 per annum; and it was ascertained (with all the accuracy that such a thing would admit) that 900,000 tons may yet be produced from it and which, at the average sale during the last six years of 55,000 tons per annum, would ensure about 17 years for which Mr. Clarke has a lease of greater extent. This calculated as an annuity for 17 years and after paying interest on the machinery in stock, would be worth £89,000 and the committee believe they estimate it modestly at £60,000.

Besides the colliery, Clarke owned the Orrell Post House estate and the mansion he had built there known as Orrell Mount. He also owned Crooke Hall estate and land at the Springs in Orrell and at Ashton in Makerfield. His fine collection of pictures and his library and other effects at Orrell Mount were sold but his creditors allowed him to live at Crooke Hall. The colliery was not sold but carried on under Daglish's management, the profits eventually liquidating all Clarke's debts.

John Clarke died at Crooke Hall on 9 August 1821 and he was buried in a vault, still very prominent, in UpHolland churchyard on the opposite side of the chancel to his manager Daglish. Clarke's Orrell pits were worked out during the 1830s but his Winstanley

M

Colliery only came to an end in 1852. A statement of coal worked up to April 1846 shows that 102 acres, 3 roods, 40 square yards had been worked under the 1812 lease and this had yielded £31,832 in royalties to Meyrick Bankes and his son Meyrick. The statement also shows that £1,000 was paid to Bankes as 'compensation for Waggon Roads, Coal pit brows, Roads and other trespass, the land not being made arable as required by the lease'.

When the colliery finished an area of 37 Cheshire acres of this seam known as the Third Lot had been reserved and left unworked. The western edge of this was Winstanley Park wall from the Tinker Hole Fault near New House Farm to a point near UpHolland Lodges. From here the north west boundary of the area ran through the Gardens Wood and then curved back again to the Tinker Hole Fault near the New Covert. The Tinker Hole Fault bounded the area on the south side. Large stones on the surface in Winstanley Park marked the boundaries of this area. It was thought to have been left in order to support the pleasure grounds of Winstanley Hall but several of Clarke's old shafts in the New Covert, ie at the dip side of the area, had been left open, possibly with a view to facilitating the getting of this coal at some future date. Mr G.H. Bankes and the Pemberton Colliery Co (Blundells) gave consideration to working this in the 1930s but after some abortive boring the scheme came to nothing. Eventually in 1963 the NCB worked part of it by means of tunnels driven through the Tinker Hole Fault from Summersales Colliery which was an extension of Blundells' old Pemberton Colliery.

The thickness of the seam varied between 3ft 6in and 3ft 9in. Thus the working of this seam in Winstanley begun by Clarke in 1791 only came to an end in 1966 when Summersales Colliery closed. John Clarke and even Robert Daglish would have been amazed to see the methods used by the NCB in 1966 in getting this coal compared with the methods they themselves employed. Nevertheless the total output of Clarke's Gathurst, Orrell Post and Winstanley Collieries during the early years of the nineteenth century must have been in the region of 100,000 tons per annum, a considerable business enterprise.

4.4 THE HALLIWELL - LONGBOTHOM - HUSTLER COLLIERIES

Orrell Hall Colliery

Orrell Hall Colliery had been worked for two centuries before our period by the Sherringtons. Towards the end of the seventeenth century it passed into the possession of the Prescotts, Samuel Prescott having succeeded Jeffrey Prescott before 1748 when the former leased the colliery and farm to Ralph Bradshaw, yeoman of Orrell. Bradshaw was to pay a royalty of 10d (4p) per score of 24 baskets of 122lb weight each when these were sold at 3s (15p) per score; 1½d a score when they were sold at 3s 6d (17½p) and 1s 1d (5½p) per score when the selling price went up to 4s (20p).

The colliery must have been extensively worked by the Prescotts for thirty years previous to the granting of the lease to Bradshaw as it was stated in 1759 that there were many 'old disused works, pitts and hollows in the land where great quantities of coal had been got out for above 40 years'. The estate comprised 35 acres, 2 roods, 2 poles of the Cheshire measure. The Orrell Five Feet Seam lay very near the surface over a considerable part of the estate on the north side of the Grand Dyke Fault, which threw the measures down 40yd to the south. It was in the shallow area, mostly exhausted of Orrell Five Feet that Bradshaw was working a thin seam of inferior cannel, known in the district as 'hoo' cannel which lay some 37ft below the Five Feet Seam. Not finding much profit in this and not having proved any coal on the dip side of the 40yd fault, he apparently wished to give up the lease.

With this in view, the heirs of Samuel Prescott began negotiations with John Heskin of Wrightington. They informed him that

> there was sufficient coal to supply the demands of a large sale as well by water or land carriage and could not be got or wrought out in many years and that the same lay near to the River Douglas and very convenient not only for land carriage but for exportation or carrying coast ways by flatts or vessels navigating on that river and that the same could be got to advantage with little expense and might be easily got at a little expense.

They assured Heskin that 'there were then great quantities of good coal sufficient to supply the demands of a large sale for many years' and that 'a great deal of money might be got by such coals'. But Heskin did not tell them that 'he was an entire stranger to and altogether unacquainted with collieries or the manner of managing and carrying on coal works'.

Prescott's heirs gave Heskin the impression that Bradshaw had dealt unfairly with them and for this reason they would not renew his lease. They agreed that Heskin should have a partner but not Ralph Bradshaw. It was at this stage that John Halliwell came in as Heskin's partner. He was one of the most experienced coal-masters in the district at that time. From 1728 he had been working collieries in Welch Whittle, Wrightington and Aspull and indeed a document of 1735 described him as 'John Halliwell of North Tunley in Wrightington commonly styled of the Coal Pits, Gentleman'. He was a Roman Catholic, like many others in that district, and he must have had some standing in that community as he was an executor under the will of Edward Dicconson, RC Bishop of Malla & Vicar Apostolic of the Northern Province. Dicconson who belonged to the Wrightington Hall family resided during the latter part of his life at Finch Mill House, Appley Bridge which has only recently been demolished. He lies buried in the chancel of St Wilfred's Parish Church, Standish, where there is a a monument to him.

Before Halliwell came in Heskin had met John Battye one of Prescott's heirs at 'a Publick House called Orrell Post', when Battye again repeated that 'beds or veins of coal were rather large and lay near the surface of the earth so as to be got at with little expence or trouble'. He suggested that the term of the lease should be forty years and the royalty the same as it was for Bradshaw. Some of Prescott's heirs did not agree with this and an auction of the colliery was arranged to take place at the Eagle and Child in Wigan on the 14 November 1755.

At the auction Edward Smith and John Battye, two of Prescott's heirs were joined by Ralph Bradshaw. When they and 'other persons (including Heskin and Halliwell) were assembled together, great quantities of ale, wine, punch and other strong liquors were laid on a table before them'. Smith and Battye expatiated at length on the quality and thickness of the beds of coal. They were very pressing on Halliwell

> to drink and put the liquor about, scarcely letting the glass stand still
> and when all the liquor on the table was drunk out, they called for
> and had more in great plenty from time to time and filled over-large
> glasses which were drunk at their importunity by John Halliwell and
> some of the company and by these means and a pretence that the
> terms for the bidding were drawing up and not ready, the proposed
> bidding was delayed.

Battye took Halliwell into another room where they continued to drink and it was arranged that whichever way the bidding went, Halliwell was to have a 21 year lease at a royalty of 1s (5p) per score of twenty-four baskets at a selling price of 3s (15p) and more than 1s as the selling price went up.

Halliwell said that 'if Bradshaw had not observed the conditions of the lease; the colliery would be of much less value and be greatly damaged thereby and the colliery drowned or destroyed'. Halliwell alleged afterwards that they had given him so much drink that when the terms of the letting of the farm and colliery were read over, he was so far deprived of his reason and understanding that he was not capable of reading, comprehending or understanding the same.

He was 'incapable of writing his name properly although he was a good writer'. The terms he agreed to were as mentioned by Battye earlier on, plus £39 a year for the farm and, what had not been mentioned previously, a certain rent equivalent to a get of 60,000 baskets per year or 3,368 tons per year which is equal to 11.3 tons per working day and would require four colliers to work the pit.

The outcome of all this was that Halliwell found the area of shallow Orrell Five Feet Coal north of the 40yd fault more or less completely worked out. It was because of this that Bradshaw had attempted to work the thin seam of bastard cannel which he had found 37ft below the Five Feet Seam.

The Five Feet workings being drowned, Halliwell contracted with Thomas Owen, Lord of the Manor, for liberty to drive a sough to the old workings through his land. This sough cost him £200. He also carried out much boring without finding any coal (probably because he did not bore deep enough). Previous to this 'Samuel Prescott and Martha Prescott, his mother had caused many parts of the demesnes and other land to be bored and searched for coal in or about the year 1747 without finding any'. Halliwell heard about this but they flatly refused to give him any information derived from the borings. Halliwell complained that all the mines in the demesnes had long before the time they entered into their contract 'been entirely wrought out and that there were no mines or beds of coal which could be wrought'. This would appear to show that the relationship between the two Orrell seams, the Five Feet and the Four Feet was not understood at that time. Halliwell persevered however, and by dint of much boring (he put 130 boreholes down) proved the line of the 40yd fault, the Five Feet on the dip side of it and the Orrell Four Feet on the Orrell Hall or rise side of the fault, where the Prescotts and Bradshaws had previously worked the Orrell Five Feet and the thin cannel seam. The boring records mention: 'cannel in the barn meadow ·6 yards 1ft. 10in. to bottom of it and the coal lies about 52 yard deeper' and 'Auger hole deep to the bottom of the coal 64 yards 1ft. 4in. and 3in. in hard stone and all the coal at the above depth'.

An estimate of the profits to be made by raising 50 score of coals, or approximately 71 tons per week, was written out by Halliwell:

	£	s	d
To getting 50 score at 1s. per score	2	10	0
To banking, winding etc. at 4d. per score		16	8
Engine man		10	0
Lords part after £100 per annum	2	0	0
	5	16	8
Value of 50 score at 3/3d. per score or 1½d. per basket	8	2	6
Remains towards the engine and sinking	2	5	10
Value of 50 score if sold at 2d. per basket	10	16	8
Cost of working	5	16	8
Neat value	5	0	0

Halliwell sank or opened out an old pit in the shallow area to start with, and this was known as Gerrards Pit. Bartons Pit was opened at the same time. This was on the opposite side of Springs Road to Orrell Hall farm yard and 40yd from the road. It was 14yd deep to the Orrell Five Feet, the first coal being raised there on 11 June 1763 a week after Gerrards Pit went into production. No doubt they were splitting old pillars left by Bradshaw and Prescott.

In spite of Halliwell's assertion about there being no coal, the Five Feet was proved by boreholes. In the Stone Delph Hey, near John Rigby Grammar School at 11 yards 0ft 0in, behind Orrell Hall in the Hall (or Little Meadow) it was 14yds 2ft 9in and in the Barn Hey, now traversed by the M6 Motorway, it was found at a depth of 6ft 10in. The Mine Workings Record plan, made by Lancashire County Council during the construction of the M6 Motorway, shows old workings under the motorway in that area at 10ft, 12ft, 14ft, 15ft, and 24ft. The coal in the crushed pillars was found to be 3ft thick.

At the same time as he was opening Gerrards and Bartons Pits, Halliwell had sunk an engine pit in the demesnes to the Four Feet Seam, and this began raising coal from 9 July 1763. The Bye Pit was sunk also in the demesnes 'next to the Engine Pitt' and this wound coal from January 1764.

In the year 1772 3,079 baskets at 150lb to the basket were consumed at the pumping engine boiler. This works out at 206 tons in the year or about 100lb per hour, allowing for 12 hours working per day and banking the boiler fire during the 12 hours the engine was stopped. It is assumed that the engine only worked 12 hours a day as only one engine man was employed. No doubt a quantity of slack was mixed in with the coal but there is no record of this. The smallest Cochran Vertical Boiler in common use fifty years ago, 7ft high by 3ft diameter and with a working

53 Orrell Hall

pressure of over 100 lb/in^2 used 70lb of coal per hour.

Allowances were made against royalty payments for workmens' concessionary coal (amounting to 2 baskets of 150lb weight per week for each collier), hiring workmen, way-candles, new riddles and new sledges etc. On 14 December 1771 Joshua Hodson was allowed 1 score 13 baskets of 122lb weight for way-drawing 20yd in Higham's Pit. John Hodson was allowed 3 score 17 baskets for 'entering' or opening the seam from the shaft at Park Pit when the 42yd deep Park Pit was newly sunk. He was also allowed 1 score 13 baskets for a new riddle and the same for a new sledge. He drove the north-west endgate in the Park Pit for seventeen weeks and produced approximately three tons per day. Assuming that the endgate was the usual 5ft in width and the coal 4ft 6in thick, it would be driven approximately 125yd, which may be assumed to be the limit of that particular pit. On 19 June 1773 Hodson was paid extra for 'way-drawing to ye end of 60 yards'.

This John Hodson is very probably the father of Betty Hodson, the Lancashire Collier Girl whose story appeared in the *Gentleman's Magazine* of March 1795.

The average output of the colliery per week was 145 tons, assuming that 50 weeks per year were worked for six years back from 30 September 1769 and a further 15 weeks back to 9 June, when Gerrard's Pit started sending coal.

Up to September 1769 the colliery was known as Orrell Hall Colliery, but from that date its name was changed to the Orrell Fire Engine Colliery. New account books, beginning with No 1, were introduced, but unfortunately the first four half-yearly accounts covering the period October 1769 to October 1771 are missing. The fact that the colliery was renamed, and that the new set of accounts show that coal was supplied to the engine boiler fire, would seem to indicate that the fire engine, or Newcomen engine, was introduced at the colliery in 1769. In the accounts previous to 1769 a customary allowance of coal is shown for the engine, but this was an allowance against royalty payments. It is possible that Halliwell had originally installed a water-powered pumping engine fed from Ackhurst Brook, as he already possessed one of these, which had previously drained his Aspull cannel pits. However, as the workings became more extensive, draining a larger area, he must have found it necessary in 1769 to replace the water wheel by a steam engine.

The names of the fields on an estate map of 1770 give a good indication of where some of these pits were situated. Barton's pits would probably be in Bartons Meadow on the south side of the junction of Springs Road and Latham Lane, near to where the British Road Services garage is now situated. Gerrard's Pit and Bradshaw's Double Pit were sunk in the Gorsey Mans Hey, which is the field opposite to Leigh Cottage, and it can be assumed that the Park Pit was in the Park Field on the Kitt Green side of the Old Engine public house near Eton Way. No doubt Great Carr Pit was in Great Carr Heys somewhere near Derwent Road on the new housing estate off Gathurst road and the Engine Pit and its companion Bye Pit would be situated in the Engine Field, now covered with a street known as Oxford Road.

As the accounts show, Halliwell continued to work his colliery up to the end of December 1776. The Orrell Hall estate had been purchased by Holt Leigh on 5 October 1769 and soon afterwards Halliwell claimed that he had paid for 8,927 scores of baskets more than he had actually got before the purchase by Holt Leigh. Arbitrators Ralph Peters of Hindley and John Aspinall of Preston gave judgement that 'John Hallywell had no right, title, claim or demand upon Holt Leigh for the coal he had paid the previous owners for, but had not got' and on the contrary he was ordered to pay Holt Leigh £556.

Halliwell died in 1770 and left his collieries and mining equipment to his son, Denis. However, the Orrell Hall lease was due to terminate in 1776, and by this time John Hustler, chairman of the Leeds and Liverpool Canal, had entered into negotiations with Holt Leigh with a view to establishing a large colliery concern on his estate. This roused resentment in Denis Halliwell and in a letter dated 8 August 1777 written by Hustler to Holt Leigh, the former said

> we forgot to mention yesterday that as Halliwell seems to be hostile in the proceedings about giving up the coal mine, he may probably fill

Table 2. John Halliwell's Orrell Collieries

Name of pit	Date opened	Date closed or end of accounts	Total output tons	number of weeks worked	Average output per week tons	Acreage (statute) worked assuming 60% extraction
Gerrard's Pit	4 June 1763	7 Apr 1764	1,459	43	33.9	probably working pillars
Barton's Pit	17 June 1763	17 Nov 1765	928	126	7.4	,, ,,
Engine Pit	9 July 1763	29 Apr 1765	3,990	93	42.9	1.16
Bradshaw's Double Pit	12 Sept 1763	21 July 1764	399	44	9.0	probably working pillars
Bye Pit	28 Jan 1764	30 Nov 1765	3,688	74	49.8	1.07
Ackers' Pit	1 Apr 1765	30 Sept 1768	7,434	183	40.3	2.13
Oval Pit	27 May 1765	30 Sept 1769	11,020	226	48.7	3.22
Shuttle-Le-Will Pit	23 June 1765	30 Sept 1769	8,248	170	48.4	2.41
Hodson's Pit	5 May 1766	30 Sept 1769	7,590	179	42.5	2.22
Highams Pit	5 Oct 1771	24 Dec 1773	6,026	114	52.8	1.76
Berry's Pit	5 Oct 1771	1 Oct 1774	9,849	154	63.9	2.86
Park Pit	11 Apr 1772	3 June 1775	10,822	170	63.7	3.16
Great Carr Pit	7 May 1774	30 Dec 1776	8,724	136	64.1	2.55
Know Pit	16 Dec 1775	13 Jan 1776	141	5	28.2	an unsuccessful pit
Know Shift Pit	4 May 1776	28 Dec 1776	2,545	35	72.7	probably not worked out

NB Up to 1 Oct 1769 the colliery was known as Orrell Hall Colliery, and afterwards, when new accounts were kept, as Orrell Fire Engine Colliery. Account books No 1-4 up to 5 Oct 1771 are missing. From 31 Dec 1776 the colliery was taken over by Hustler, Hardcastle & Chadwick.

up the Engine Pit or otherwise damage it so as to leave it unfit for us
to put down another which might be a bad consequence. We therefore
desire you will be pleased to take the proper steps to prevent him from
doing this by giving him notice that it must be left open and undamaged
either in the shaft or in the works below and please to appoint some
propper person to see that he complies with it.

Hustler had two partners Thomas Hardcastle of Bradford and
John Chadwick, ironmaster of Burgh near Chorley. They duly
took over the Orrell Hall Colliery after the expiration of Halliwell's lease and worked the Four Feet Seam until it was exhausted.

Dean, Ayrefield, Naylor's Estate and Sephton's Estate Collieries

A twenty-one year lease, dated 20 January 1775, from Holt
Leigh, son of Alexander Leigh, gave John Longbothom of Hargreaves, Lancashire, the engineer who built the first part of the
Leeds and Liverpool canal, the right to work the Four Feet or
Lower Mine and what remained of the Upper or Five Feet Mine
under the Dean Estate in UpHolland. Before this time, the Four
Feet had remained unworked, but the Five Feet Seam had been
worked by Alexander Leigh, Culshaw and others. It would appear
that Longbothom worked this seam until the opening of his engine pit in January 1776. Under the terms of the lease, he was to
have slack, free of royalty, for use in the boiler of this fire engine.
He was to have the usual customary rights and also running powers
over the wooden railroad from Jackson's Colliery (later Blundells')
down Dean Wood to the canal. The purpose of erecting the fire
engine would be to work the deeper mine as the Five Feet lay
near the surface and actually outcropped on the estate. It was
drained into Dean Brook by means of soughs. The seam was worked presumably from a shaft in the Coal Pit Hey and also from the
'Day Eye in the wood' and the 'Day Eye near the lime kiln'.

John Langshaw's name appears early in 1776 as working these
pits, so either he was a partner of Longbothom or he had sub-
leased the seam. Longbothom's accounts of coal production 'from
the commencement to the opening of the Engine Pit' have survived but these are dealt with under the heading 'Methods of working coal'.

The Engine Pit must have been about ninety yards deep and
the engine itself would be of the Newcomen type. The certain
rent was only £50 per year and the royalty was 1s 8d (8½p) per
'score of Baskets of coals each score to consist of 26 baskets and
each basket to contain 140 lb'. 3,600 score of baskets was allowed
in satisfaction of the certain rent. This would be equal to an annual
output of 5,832 tons. All the coal had to be 'riddled with riddles

having squares or meshes of ¾ in. so that all coal that passes the riddle is deemed to be slack or culm'. Longbothom was at liberty to convert the slack into 'cinders' (coke).

In 1774, Longbothom, together with John Hustler, had taken a lease of the Orrell Four Feet Seam in part of Charles Prescott's Ayrefield estate, but very few particulars of this colliery are known except that it was important enough to have a wagonway constructed to the canal.

On the 17 October 1775 Longbothom leased the Orrell Five Feet Seam under an estate belonging to Holt Leigh and known as 'Naylor's' on the north side of Orrell Road between Orrell Post and Spencer's Lane near Abbey Lakes. This had previously been leased for 14 years in 1769 to Ralph Bradshaw and Partners. As far as Longbothom's lease was concerned, the terms and conditions were similar to those for the Dean Colliery except that the certain rent was £300 per annum.

However, shortly after this, Longbothom seems to have got into financial difficulties, for in September 1776 he is in arrears with the rent for both the Dean and Orrell Collieries. He owed rent for a year-and-a-half on the Dean Colliery, one year's rent on the Orrell Colliery and 'scorage of coals from old pits at the Dean', which altogether amounted to £436 10s 9d (£436.54). In addition to this, he owed Holt Leigh £217 11s 4d (£217.56) for bricks, timber, cottage rents and a promissary note that bounced. All this resulted in Longbothom's lease being terminated and the same areas of coal being leased to Hustler, Hardcastle and Chadwick on an entirely different system of royalty payments. They were to pay a certain rent of £500 per annum with a mine rent of £380 per acre for the Five Feet Seam and £260 per acre for the Four Feet Seam. The minimum or certain rent was increased to £900 per year in January 1788, making it necessary to work two acres of Four Feet and one acre of Five Feet to cover it, which would give an annual minimum production figure of about 39,000 tons.

The minimum rent was again raised to £1,000 in 1791 and progressively to £2,500 per annum in 1801. By December 1805, at the end of the thirty-year lease, royalty amounting to £26,331 had been paid for the Four Feet Seam and £14,780 for the Five Feet Seam.

Assuming the former seam to have been 3.7ft thick and the latter 4.5ft thick, and calculating it back to tons, we get an average annual production figure for the thirty years of 18,767 tons of Orrell Five Feet and 39,745 tons of Orrell Four Feet, an average for both seams of 58,512 tons. However, to cover the minimum rent of £2,500 paid during the last five years and assuming the proportion of Four Feet to Five Feet worked as two to one, it would have been necessary to raise no less than 106,500 tons per year.

During the working of the collieries, John and Jeffrey Langshaw seemed to be involved, but exactly how is not clear. They may have been sub-lessees or raising contractors under Hustler and Co.

John Hustler senior has already been mentioned under the section on the Leeds and Liverpool canal and he belonged to a remarkable Quaker family. During the latter part of the eighteenth and early part of the nineteenth centuries they occupied:

> a most prominent place in the doings of the town and neighbourhood [of Bradford], in fact did more in their day towards the extension of its trade and the improvement of Bradford than anyone else. For upwards of a century they were the leading woolstaplers of the town, and... were occasionally styled merchants, by which occupation the family amassed an immense wealth.

John Hustler senior, the partner of Hardcastle & Chadwick in the Orrell Collieries, was born in the year 1713. After his death in 1790 his son, William, took over the collieries and other businesses. Long before this, in 1780, John Chadwick had died and his widow had opted out of the colliery partnership. Thomas Hardcastle, however, seems to have played an active role in the collieries, at least in the early days. William Hustler was an authority on botany and he was:

> the intimate friend of Sir Robert Holt Leigh who persuaded him to work the Orrell Collieries on his estate near Wigan in Lancashire. This for many years was a most lucrative concern but ultimately was worked out.

However lucrative it may have been later, there were difficulties in the early days. On 7 September 1779 Hustler wrote to Holt Leigh informing him that his partner, Hardcastle, had asked him to advance him £400 for paying royalty on the colliery:

> which he cannot raise out of the trade till about Xmas when we call in our coal debts at Liverpool. I send this to beg thy indulgence till then which I hope thou wilt think a reasonable request when I have informed thee that we have advanced above £8,000 into the works and Trade. That we have already paid more than we have got coals to the amount of in thy estate, that the great part of these are unsold owing to the Calamity of the Times and obstructions to our demands abroad from the want of shipping and hands to navigate them. That we have laid out large sums in making provision for carrying on a large trade abroad in coals which when peace is restored we expect will take of twice the quantity we are bound by our lease and produce then a much larger profit annually than our stipulated rent. Add to this the great

difficulty of getting money in although upon the best securities, and my Friend Leigh (I cannot have a doubt) will think my request not unreasonable; and the more especially as it has been customary for gentlemen in the opening and establishing of such great works as this to think it their interest to give considerable indulgence in the capital Rent till the capital Trade comes about when thou may depend on the utmost punctuality from us. We are making the utmost effort to retain correspondents for taking of our old stock of coals and opening a large future demand and hope thou wilt not think it good policy or precedent to throw any discouragement upon our ardour at this unexampled difficult season as a gentleman of thy large fortune cannot be at a loss for supplying such a sum without much inconvenience. I intend to be at Wigan the next week when I shall hope to meet with thy acquiescence with this request and with kind regards thy assured friend.
John Hustler.

William Hustler died of fever in 1801 and left his property to his three children, who were made wards of his younger brother John, and he subsequently bought their shares in the business. When the colliery lease came up for renewal in 1806 Maffey says

Sir Robert Holt Leigh would not grant a renewal of the colliery lease to anyone who did not bear the name of Hustler, consequently William's younger brother as the childrens' guardian became the proprietor of the half of the Orrell Colliery.

Besides the collieries at Orrell Hall, Ayrefield, Naylor's Estate and the Dean, Hustlers worked the coal between Abbey Lakes and Moor Road and also in the Sephton Road-St James's Road area. They constructed wagonways. (These are described in the section on that subject). In the report of the 1842 Commission enquiring into child and female labour employed underground, Hustlers are said to have ninety-one men and eight women over the age of 21, eleven boys and four girls under 21 and over 13 and eighteen boys and two girls under 13.

John Hustler died aged 71 years at a house he had recently bought at York on the 18 January 1842. His widow, who was his second wife, was a minister of the Society of Friends for forty years, and his first wife was Elizabeth Pease of the great Durham Quaker family of industrialists. He left one son, John Mildred Hustler, the child of his second wife, Mary Mildred, and he was:

as gay as his father was sedate. A popular youth of good address he had the entree of the best society and was easily misled. He was very fond of sport and was of an excitable and wilful disposition. His extravagance brought him and his father into serious financial difficulty.

In the diary of Edward Pease, the latter refers to him as follows:

1846. Saturday November 21st. Morning commenced with very animated converse on the part of Mildred Hustler respecting coals and mining, in which every faculty of his busy immature judgement seemed

turned with fullest confidence of success. When I remember the dignity
of his grandfather, his quiet religious mind maturing that great work
the Leeds and Liverpool canal and his pious dedicated grandmother
Christiana Hustler and his worthy father my brother-in-law, John Hustler, I could only lament over this youth.

Nevertheless, Mildred Hustler had taken into partnership William Hill Brancker of Liverpool and, at the time that Edward Pease
was lamenting over him, they were engaged in sinking a new colliery to be known as Orrell Colliery, although it was just inside
the Pemberton boundary at Walthew House and not in the area
we are considering. A date stone on an engine house at these new
pits bore the inscription 'J.M. Hustler & Co. 1846'.

However, soon after this, in 1849, John Mildred Hustler died
at the age of thirty-three, unmarried 'just as he was endeavouring
to retrieve the family fortunes'. It was about this time, or shortly
afterwards, that the old collieries in the Orrell belt came to a close,
having worked out all the available coal.

4.5 LOFTHOUSE, JARRATT & COMPANY'S COLLIERIES

In 1788, 18 acres of the 'Orrell Four Feet or Delf Mine' in the
estate of Michael and John Harvey, at what became known as
Harvey House, was leased for a term of twenty-one years to John
Jarratt, merchant of Bradford, John Lofthouse, a coal merchant
of Liverpool, Joseph Dawson of Fole in Yorkshire described as a
'Dissenting Minister' and John Hardy a Bradford lawyer. The two
latter became partners with Hird in the great Low Moor Ironworks
and Collieries at Bradford and Dawson is said to have paid his
colliers on a Sunday morning before entering the pulpit to preach.

The lease was the customary one for the district at the time.
The lessees had power to put boreholes down, sink pit shafts,
drive soughs, erect pumping engines, smithies, workshops etc and
to construct 'railed waggon ways' over any part of the surface
leased. The royalty was £260 per Cheshire acre of the seam.

As the Five Feet Seam lay very near to the surface, it was considered doubtful whether its quality was suitable for the Liverpool
market. If it was found to be good enough, the lessees had power
to work it and the royalty was to be determined by two indepen-
dent experts. In addition to the Harvey House coal, they took
out two other leases in our area. One was for the Four Feet Seam
100yd deep under Pearson-Liveseys estate, where the Five Feet
Seam had previously been worked from 1773 to 1785 by Samuel
Bold, Halliwell's old enemy Ralph Bradshaw of Orrell, James Brad-

shaw of Parbold and William Briggs wine merchant of Preston. The other was for the Four Feet Seam from the outcrop to the Douglas in Holt's estate in Shevington on the western side of Gathurst Road.

They first produced coal in 1791 and during the following year they raised about 10,000 tons. This figure is an estimate based on the number of colliers employed by the firm as given in the Land Tax Returns for Orrell. The output was doubled in 1793 to about 20,000 tons but in 1794 dropped to 5,000 and working seems to have ceased temporarily in 1795. However, in the following year, they must have raised about 30,000 tons and by 1799 had topped 40,000 tons. After 1799 there is very little information available. The Land Tax Returns for 1804 do not mention Lofthouse and Jarratt but a new name, Taylor, appears in the list as employing fifteen colliers. It is very likely that Taylor was their agent as Robinson's name is given for Hustler's colliery as employing fifty colliers, and Robinson was Hustler's colliery agent and manager. Even Taylor's name is not seen again but the small firm of Langshaw appears. They may possibly have taken over Lofthouse and Jarratt's colliery, but they also seem to have been sub-lessees of Hustler.

In any case in 1798 Jarratt, Lofthouse, Dawson and Hardy had become partners with William Hustler of Bradford, wool stapler, Jonathan Peckover of Wisbech and late of Bradford, banker, James Monk of Burscough, timber merchant, Henry Ellam of Standish, formerly Blundells' Colliery manager and William Robinson of Ayrefield House, UpHolland, Hustler's colliery manager. This rather unlikely partnership took out a lease on 26 Jan 1798 of every seam of coal 'already opened and found or which hereafter shall be found' in the Standish family estates in Standish, Shevington, Worthington, Coppull, Duxbury and Wigan. The part of the Standish estates in our area was that bounded by Gathurst Lane on the west, the River Douglas on the south, the Pemberton Fault on the east and the outcrop of the Orrell Four Feet Seam running east to the Pemberton Fault from the present Blackledge's Garage in Gathurst Lane, Shevington. However, German had already leased a part of the coal under this and he was allowed to retain it. In the lease of all this coal from Charles Townley of Townley and Edward Towneley Standish of Standish Hall, Dawson is no longer described as a 'Dissenting Minister' but as 'of Royds Hall in the Parish of Bradford, Iron Master'. Jarratt and Hardy, having made their money, are described as 'Gentlemen' not as merchant and lawyer as ten years previously.

With all this in hand and the great Yorkshire iron and coal concerns to attend to, it is no wonder that we see very little more of them in Orrell.

4.6 WOODCOCK AND HALIBURTON'S COLLIERY CONCERN

In January 1793 Alexander Haliburton of Inverkeithing, Fife, was appointed manager of Haigh Foundry which was owned by Lord Balcarres. Haliburton's association with that works continued until 1826. He also had charge of Lord Balcarres's collieries at Haigh, although from 1813, if not earlier, he had engaged in the colliery business at Orrell on his own account, with a partner, Thomas Woodcock. This state of affairs did not seem to worry Alexander, the sixth Earl of Balcarres, but after he died in 1825, his son James succeeded to the Earldom and estates, and he seems to have been rather dubious about Haliburton. The result was that in March 1826, Haliburton resigned his position as colliery agent at Haigh and he also withdrew from Haigh Foundry in which he said he had been a partner 'until the death of the late Lord Balcarres'.

A note by the new lord on the back of this letter stated: 'from Mr Haliburton about his engagement at Haigh. He disclaims being a partner and now does his duty all for Love, but which I can by no means agree with'. Haliburton defended himself by saying

the concerns in which I have been engaged in the neighbourhood are the same as they have been for nearly twenty years, in no instance clashing with or at variance with the affairs of Haigh, but on the contrary, in several respects, favourable to them.

Haliburton's partner, Thomas Woodcock, came from a Wigan family of bankers, lawyers and businessmen. He lived at 'The Elms' in Wigan Lane which now belongs to Wigan and Leigh Hospitals, and at Newburgh House, Newburgh, now known as Woodcock Hall. His monument in the Parish Church at Wigan states that 'for upwards of forty-three years he was a banker in Wigan'.

Their first lease in the Orrell belt was from Meyrick Bankes of Winstanley Hall. It was dated 24 April 1813 and was for 21 Cheshire acres of Orrell Four Feet under part of the Holland House estate at UpHolland, the term being 21 years. They had the usual powers to construct 'any wagon road or other roads' and at first permission was granted for the lessees to turn their water into Blundells' Chain Colliery workings for it to be pumped at their Engine Pit, but Blundell naturally objected and it was not allowed.

They were to leave support for the two mansion houses on the estate, Holland House (now a club) and Holland Grove, which for many years has been a laundry. Unfortunately the seam outcropped before it reached Holland Grove and it would seem that there was less than 21 acres to work. If there were the full 21 acres there would be about 226,800 tons to get allowing for 10 per cent loss.

The minimum or certain rent was £630 per year and the mine rent £420 per Cheshire acre which means that they had to work 1½ acres or 16,200 tons per year, again allowing for 10 per cent loss, to cover the certain rent.

A plan of the workings had to be kept and indeed this was the usual thing. James Marsh, a surveyor or dialer, sent Holt Leigh a bill in March 1783 for making up his royalty plans—

	£	s	d
To 11 days assisting to measure coals got by Mr Holme in Nailors estate in Orrell		11	0
Board wages at Mr Rigby's [the Stag Inn at Orrell Post]		11	0
To ale, bread and cheese given to assistants		7	6
To three journeys to Mr Holmes to fix a time for Measuring		6	0
	1	15	6

The lessees had the usual permission to dig clay for making bricks and gravel, sand and stone as long as it was for colliery use. It would appear that they had started in the coal trade before they acquired any coal mines as the flats on the canal belonging to them are mentioned. This lease seems to have been revised or extended on 1 May 1817 with a term of 21 years from that date.

Their next lease in the Orrell belt was dated 1 April 1815, and was for the Orrell Four Feet and the Orrell Five Feet under the Bridgewater Trustees' land at Lamberhead Green. The famous Hundred Year Trust had been set up under the terms of the will of the Third Duke of Bridgewater (the Canal Duke) after he died in 1803. At the time Woodcock and Haliburton's lease was granted, the trustees were:

The Rt Hon Sir Archibald MacDonald Bart late Chief Baron of H.M. Court of Exchequer, the Most Rev Father in God Edward Venables by Divine Providence Archbishop of York, Robert Haldane Bradshaw of Worsley Hall and the Rt Hon George Granville Leveson, Marquis of Stafford, Beneficiary for life under the Will.

MacDonald and Bradshaw are commemorated in streets bearing their names at Lamberhead Green, the nearby Loch Street being named after James Loch, a later trustee.

Altogether the area leased comprised 104 statute acres but 18 acres of this was part of the Summersales estate which the partners could not have worked, as Blundells worked it from 1839 onwards. The coal lay at a much greater depth than that in the Orrell belt proper, and this may be the reason they did not tackle it.

The certain rent was only £200 per Cheshire acre and the mine rent was £80 per Cheshire acre per foot thick. This seems to be the first time that a footage rent was introduced in the Orrell area. If any pillars were left, they had to be paid for at the same rate. The lessees were at liberty to sink pit shafts on any part of the land leased and to drive soughs through any other land belonging to the trustees.

They also had powers to erect whimseys, smithies, cabins, stables, coke ovens and steam engines in any part of the land and to use the brooks and construct reservoirs for the boilers of the steam engines; they could burn the slack into coke and stack it on the premises until it was sold; they also had power to construct wagon roads or any other roads over any part of the land; at the termination of the lease they were to have the machinery and any materials. The lessees also had to 'observe and keep a good and true water level in each of the mines from the deepest Engine Pit which shall be made or sunk on the said lands', and they were to leave substantial ranges of pillars to support the water levels and shafts.

As little damage as possible was to be done to the land and none at all to the buildings. The pits and wagon roads had to be fenced and the latter were to be provided with gates where required. If there was any subsidence, loss of coal, inundations of water etc, the lessees had to allow the trustees' agents to go down and inspect the workings.

At the termination of the lease, the pits were to be filled in (unless the trustees required them for further working) the wagon roads were to be levelled and all gaps in hedges and other fences made up. Farm tenants were to be compensated for loss of crops etc. A third lease was taken out in October 1822, from Richard Longworth Perceval, for the Orrell Four Foot and Five Foot Seams under the Walthew House estate. The term of the lease was 30 years and the royalty payable was £200 and £330 per Cheshire acre for the Four Foot and Five Foot Seams respectively. £38 per acre per foot thick was to be paid for inferior seams. Unfortunately the Pemberton Fault shatter belt ran through the leasehold, cutting off the two Orrell seams. What little there was of these seams was worked together with some cannel in the fault zone but the colliery only had a short life. Woodcock and Haliburton's Collieries in the Orrell belt are said to have closed about the year 1840, after which they opened pits in the Gidlow Lane

54 A Basket Pit (No 6) at Kitt Green, originally sunk by Woodcock and Haliburton under their 1822 lease of the Walthew estate. Although very damaged, this photograph, taken before 1890, is the only one known of an Orrell colliery at work *(R. Stanton)*

area of Wigan. The number of colliers employed at their Orrell pits during the 1820s indicates an annual output in the region of 25,000 tons. Their business seems to have prospered, for in the 1830s we find Haliburton living at Whitley Hall, Wigan, a large house built for the Holt-Leigh family, and Woodcock living at Newburgh House.

4.7 THOMAS CLAUGHTON'S ORRELL COLLIERY

This worked the Orrell Four Feet Seam under Sir William Gerard's land at the western end of Tracks Lane, under part of Greenslate Farm and also under the land between Greenslate Road and the outcrop, two-thirds of the way along Sandy Lane. It was a relatively small area and the colliery appears to have had a short life of about eight years, being opened in 1811-12 and closed in 1820. The depth of the deepest of the pit-shafts could not have been more than 40yd and judging by the maximum number of colliers given in the Land Tax Returns, the output was around 12,000 tons per annum.

Thomas Claughton lived at Haydock Lodge, and later on at Golborne Park and was related to the Leghs of Lyme, who owned the Haydock and Newton Estates. He exercised his right of burial in the Legh Chapel at Wigan Parish Church by having his agent interred there in 1817. Claughton had made many purchases of land, and more than two years after his bankruptcy in March 1824, his extensive estates and coal interests were advertised for sale. These included the manors of Haughton and Southworth, one half part of the manor of Hesketh with Beconsall and freehold and leasehold estates and collieries in Middleton, Arbury, Southworth, Orford, Fearnhead, Ashton, Sankey, Pemberton and Liverpool. His most important colliery at this time was Ashtons Green in which he had a third share. This was an extensive and well-equipped colliery with three steam winding-engines, four whimseys, two 'lifting' or pumping engines and a 'railroad' to the Sankey Canal.

He was the sole owner of the Edge Green Colliery and estate at Golborne and the Stone House Colliery and estate near Smithy Brook at Pemberton. The collieries were said to be in full work and the requisite machinery complete and in good repair. In 1822 Claughton had constructed a wagon road from Stone House Colliery to the canal at the Pottery in Wigan. The pier head he erected there for loading the canal boats with coal from the wagons was taken over by Meyrick Bankes of the Winstanley Collieries some years after Claughton's bankruptcy and it became well-known early this century as 'Wigan Pier'.

At Liverpool Claughton owned two coal yards. One was situated in Gibraltar Street with a frontage of 350ft on to the Leeds and Liverpool canal and it contained an office and a weighing machine. The other coal yard was by the canal between Clement Street and Edward Street.

CHAPTER FIVE

Conclusions

The industrial archaeologist visiting the Orrell coalfield would find, at first glance, very few obvious remains of extensive coal workings. Much is said in television programmes and in newspaper articles about the 'scars of the industrial revolution' but our coalfield has escaped these.

There are no colliery dirt tips or heaps (wrongly and persistently referred to since the Aberfan disaster as 'coal tips' and even more incorrectly as 'slag tips') for the simple reason that only the cleanest and best quality seams were worked in those early days, others for the most part being unsaleable. Even the slack, although of the purest quality, was often left underground and there are tens of thousands of tons of the best Orrell Four Feet and Orrell Five Feet slack stowed in the old workings in Orrell and Winstanley, the coal having been riddled at the working face or filled into baskets by means of forks.

That some seams, worked extensively in Wigan during the second half of the nineteenth century, were not looked upon with much favour earlier on is clear from a letter dated 8 July 1837 sent to Lord Balcarres of Haigh Hall, Wigan, by William Peace his colliery manager. After stating that Mr Henry Wood had leased the coal under Whitley and Bank House at the north end of Wigan town, he says 'the estates in question will yield principally Common Coal of a very inferior description, the mines lying near the surface being the Wigan five feet mine the Wigan four feet mine and the Wigan nine feet mine'.

It was the extensive working of these and other seams of 'common coal' that made it necessary, from the middle of the nineteenth century up to the 1930s, to employ the many hundreds of 'pit brow lasses' on the picking belts that Lancashire was noted for. Also after about 1860 many washeries were set up to remove the dirt from the slack and all this dirt was tipped near the colliery surface works to form the eyesores we see today.

The only remnants of the mining industry in the Orrell field apart from the many filled up shafts and workings encountered during the construction of motorways, sewer tunnels etc are sough entrances and the sites of wagon roads.

Regarding soughs, all except one are in Dean Wood, the other being just inside Winstanley Park wall on Rylance Mill Farm at Pony Dick.

Several shafts sunk by Clarke are still open in the New Covert area of Winstanley Park, including that of the disused pumping station of Makerfield Water Board. Clarke's Engine and Bye Pits with their concrete caps are to be seen on either side of the Wigan to Liverpool railway line a quarter of a mile east of the old pumping station.

Another Makerfield Water Board shaft previously used to supply Orrell with water is Blundells' Chain Colliery Engine Pit off Gathurst Road and 350yd north-west of the Old Engine public house. The small pit-bank of the Chain Colliery No 5 Pit can be seen 300yd due west of this public house and may be approached by a public footpath from the pumping station. There is no doubt that the public house derived its name either from Halliwell's pumping engine or from Blundell's.

Very few remains of the wagon roads are to be found. Gathurst main-line railway bridge still incorporates the arch under which Hustler's wagon-road ran, although the floor has been raised. Proceeding southward from this archway along the line of the wagon-road through Gathurst Wood, one travels for six hundred yards up a steady incline to a point near the Bird 'ith Hand public house. Along this incline, a number of stone block sleepers are scattered about and quite recently a fish-bellied rail was found. Up to a short while ago before the tide of building advanced and the Skelmersdale link with the M6 Motorway was constructed, embankments along this line were visible 200yd south-east of the Old Engine public house and south of Orrell Road 150yd west of Abbey Lakes Hotel grounds. An embankment along the north side of Bispham Hall grounds shows the line of the 1840 extension of Hustler's wagon-road to the Whittle Pit at Brownlow, Bispham.

Clarke's wagon-road may be traced south from a point where the pierhead was situated, 150yd west of the canal bridge in the village of Crooke, half a mile east of Gathurst along the Douglas valley. The bridge which carries the Wigan to Southport main line railway over the wagon-road is still there and the line of the wagon-road can be traced towards the huge Heinz food factory for a further three quarters of a mile.

Nothing more can now be seen of this line for the next one and three quarter miles, but then one comes to a length of half a mile between hedges on the north west side of Winstanley park and marked on the OS map as Hall Lane. The best way to approach this is to go south-east for 400yd from Orrell railway station along Winstanley Road and the line of the wagon-road is plainly seen on the east side of the road between blocks of semi-detached houses. Proceeding east along this track for six hundred yards just under the M6 Motorway bridge the searcher will be rewarded by the sight of stone block sleepers more or less in their original positions.

Traces of both Blundells' wagon-road through Dean Wood and Longbothom's colliery road through Ayrefield wood can still be seen, now in parts used as footpaths.

The only great monument to the industrial revolution in our coalfield is the Leeds and Liverpool Canal, its bridge and the impressive double lock and toll house at Dean. The site of the locks between the canal and the River Douglas can be seen here.

An important factor which helped the Orrell area from the conservation point of view is that none of the chief landowners were absentees and were thus keen to see that their estates were well looked after and the land fully restored to agriculture on the abandonment of a colliery. Very strict conditions were laid down in all the mineral leases to ensure that this was carried out. Even gaps formed in hedges during the construction of wagon-roads had to be made up by planting quickthorn and not by the easier way of putting up posts and rails. The situation was very different however in other parts of the Wigan coalfield towards the end of the nineteenth century, when the real industrial scars began to appear. Sometimes when large collieries were established on an estate with many seams of coal to work and the prospect for the landowner of many years of very lucrative royalty payments, he was tempted to leave the district permanently and allow the working of the collieries to take precedence over everything else. This is the main reason why Ince on the east side of Wigan is such a sordid mess compared with the Orrell and Winstanley coalfield.

Of all the strangers who descended on the Orrell coalfield after the opening of the Leeds and Liverpool canal, Blundells remained the longest, staying for almost one hundred and eighty years, having extended their operations to Pemberton and other parts of the Wigan coalfield. The rest of them are long since forgotten, not even a street in Orrell bearing any of their names. They were a motley crowd of Quaker wool staplers, dissenting ministers, slave traders, privateer owners, slave trade abolitionists, West Indies plantation owners, lawyers, bankers etc and there is no doubt that they caused a big stir in the district and made a lot of money out of it, the profit per ton of coal raised often being equal to half the pithead selling price. To put this into perspective, if the NCB could do the same as these old Orrell coalmasters they would have an annual profit at present rates of something approaching £500 million.

From the opening of the Leeds and Liverpool Canal to Orrell

in 1774 to the virtual exhaustion of the coalfield in 1850, a vast amount of wealth was extracted from beneath Orrell by the local miners and their families by what must have been extremely hard, laborious and, for the women and children degrading work, requiring strength and endurance above the ordinary and this in conditions often unpleasant and dangerous to say the least.

Probably the only local people to benefit financially were the landowners, a few engineers and surveyors whose skill and knowledge made the operations successful and the shopkeepers and other tradespeople.

The greater part of the wealth produced went to build up the fortunes of the merchants from Liverpool and Bradford who owned the largest concerns. Apart from the two landed families who carried on working their collieries in the steady way they had done for many renerations, the only local colliery owners during the peak period at Orrell were Woodcock and Haliburton, even the latter having come from Scotland.

We look in vain for any evidence of 'good works' by these people, for they neither founded churches, chapels, Sunday schools, day schools, alms houses or other charities and apart from Blundells their names are long since forgotten. Blundell's name is only remembered because of their connection with mining at Pemberton up to recent times and the many benefactions they gave there at a later period than we are considering.

Reflecting upon the laborious conditions in which the coal of Orrell was produced the words written by Thomas Carlyle spring to mind. Carlyle was a young man when the Orrell collieries were at their peak:

> Venerable to me is the hard hand, venerable too is the rugged face. Is it not the face of a man living manlike. Hardly entreated brother. For us was thy back so bent, for us was thy straight limbs and figure so deformed. Thou wert our conscript on whom the lot fell and fighting our battles thou wert so marred.

APPENDIX

List of the steam engines used in the Orrell Coalfield

Date	Colliery	Owner	Notes
1769	Orrell Hall (Fire Engine Colliery)	John Halliwell	
1773	Holland House	Rev Thos Holmes	Offered to Blundell & Menzies
pre-Dec 1774	Orrell House or Saltersford	John Jackson (Blundell after 1780)	
1774	Ayrefield	Longbothom & Hustler	
1776	Dean	John Longbothom	Pumped from 90yd
pre-April 1781	Post House	William Berry	
1788	Harvey House	Jarratt & Lofthouse	
1790	Gathurst	Clarke, Roscoe & Partners	
1791	Slycroft	J. Blundell & Son	Pumped from 98yd. Ceased c1830
1791	Kitt Green	J. Blundell & Son	Pumped from 130-140yd
1792	(No 1) Winstanley	Clarke & German	Pumped 1,300 gal/hr from c80yd
1794	Winstanley (Duke's Engine Pit)	J. Blundell & Son	Possibly Orrell House engine re-erected
1796	Edge Hall	J. Blundell & Son	Pumped from 80yd
1799	Chain Colliery	Blundell & Menzies	Pumped from 120yd to adit at 43yd. Possibly Holland House engine re-erected and adapted
c1800	(No 2) Winstanley	John Clarke	
1812	Greenslates Orrell	Thos Claughton	
1813	Holland House (Orrell Four Feet)	Woodcock & Haliburton	
1822	Lamberhead Green	Woodcock & Haliburton	
1846	Walthew House	Hustler & Co	

Unfortunately no evidence has come to light on the place of manufacture of the cylinders and other main engine parts of the engines listed above, but it is very probable that those erected before 1790 were made by Wilkinson at Bersham or at Darby's Coalbrookdale Works. The pumping engine at the local Kirkless Cannel works on the north-east side of Wigan was made in 1773 by Wilkinson at Bersham.

The post-1790 engines were most probably manufactured at the important Haigh Foundry at Wigan and indeed Blundells' Pemberton engines and other local early nineteenth century pumping engines were made there.

Bibliography

MANUSCRIPTS

Wigan Public Library

Descriptive list of Holt-Leigh papers by Gershom Knight, Wigan Borough Archivist, D/DLeiT

Holt-Leigh papers, D/DLei

Dicconson papers, D/DWr

Standish papers, D/DSt

Journals of boreholes, Acc No M367-368, 3 vols

Blundells' Pemberton Colliery timebook, 1825-7

Coroner's Inquisitions, Cr/Wi

Wigan Dispensary minute books, H/R

Report of the Childrens' Employment Commission, 1841-2, HD6250.G7

Douglas Navigation accounts, D/DLei

Leeds and Liverpool Canal papers, Acc No 66376

Lancashire Record Office, Lancaster Road, Preston, Lancs

Bankes of Winstanley muniments, DDBa

Gerard of Bryn muniments, DDGe

Molyneux of Hawkley papers, DDBa

Blundell of Halsall papers, DDBB

Tithe Award plans of Orrell, Winstanley, Pemberton, Billinge and Shevington, DRL1

Plan of Orrell Hall Estate 1760, DDX/233/1

Douglas Navigation and Leeds and Liverpool Canal papers, DP175

Coroner's Inquisitions (Expenses), QSP

Land Tax Assessments, QDL

Public Record Office, Chancery Lane, London WC2

Duchy of Lancaster papers, DLI/195/10, DLI/204/0/1, DLI/205/S/27, DLI/503/(1)

John Rylands University Library, Deansgate, Manchester

The Crawford MSS

Liverpool Record Office and Local History Department, Liverpool Central Libraries, William Brown Street, Liverpool

The Roscoe papers, 920 Ros

Liverpool newspapers, 1770-1800

18th and early 19th century directories, H942.7215

The Lace Papers

Northamptonshire Record Office, Delapre Abbey, Northampton
Leases of Bridgewater coal, Ellesmere (Brackley) MSS

Hindley Public Library, Hindley, Lancs
Papers relating to the Holt-Leigh and Pemberton-Leigh families

NCB, NW Area, Plan Record Office, Anderton House, Lowton, Lancs
Old mine plans. See catalogue of plans of abandoned mines.

Bridgewater Estate Office, Worsley, Nr Manchester
Pemberton, Orrell and Winstanley estate plans

Papers in the author's possession
Blundells' colliery accounts, cost sheets, journals, reports output books, accident books, registers, conviction books, pumping books, plans, sections etc.
Various old mining notebooks
Old boring journals
Orrell Colliery manager's notebooks
Copies of Standish estate mineral leases

In other private hands
William Greener's diaries (Blundells' agent 1853-65)
Old notebook on mining in Orrell and Pemberton (1820-30)
John Halliwell's journal (18th century)
William Armstrong's reports on Blundells' collieries (mid-19th century)
Joseph Hilton (born 1849), *Orrell Octogenarian's memories of old time coal conveyance*
Edward Hilton (born 1860), *Recollections of an UpHolland collier*

ORDNANCE SURVEY
6in to one mile geological maps, 1860 and 1929 editions

PERIODICALS AND SOCIETY TRANSACTIONS
Anderson, D. 'Blundells' Collieries- The progress of the business', *Trans Hist Soc Lancs & Ches*, **116** (1964), 69
'Blundells' Collieries- Wages, disputes and conditions of work', *Trans Hist Soc Lancs & Ches*, **117**(1965), 109
'Blundells' Collieries- Technical developments 1776-1966, *Trans Hist Soc Lancs & Ches*, **119**(1967), 113
Bankes, Mrs J.H.M. 'Records of mining in Winstanley and Orrell', *Trans Lancs & Ches Antiquarian Soc*, **54**(1939), 31
'James Bankes and the Manor of Winstanley', *Trans Hist Soc Lancs & Ches*, **94**(1942), 56
'The funeral of Meyrick Bankes', *Trans Hist Soc Lancs & Ches*, **112** (1960), 159

'A nineteenth-century colliery railway', *Trans Hist Soc Lancs & Ches,* **114**(1962), 155

Killick, H. F. 'Notes on the early history of the Leeds and Liverpool Canal', *Bradford Antiquary,* **3** NS (1896-1900)

Langton, J. 'Coal output in south-west Lancashire 1590-1799', *Econ Hist Rev,* **25** no 1 (1972), 28

Lindsay, D.A.E., Earl of Crawford and Balcarres. 'Haigh Cannel', Trans Manchester Stat Soc(1933-4), 1-23 (Presidential address, centenary session vol)

Maffey, J. 'On some of the decayed families of Bradford', *Bradford Antiquary,* **1** NS (1879), 26-32

BOOKS

Ashton, T.S. and Sykes, J. *The coal industry of the eighteenth century* (Manchester 1929)

Bagley, J.J. *History of Upholland Grammar School* (Liverpool and London 1944)

Baxter, B. *Stone blocks and iron rails* (Newton Abbot 1966)

Blundell, F.O. *Old Catholic Lancashire* (1938)

Hall, E. *Miss Weeton's journal of a governess, vol1: 1807-1811, vol 2: 1811-1825* (1936 & 1939, reprinted Newton Abbot 1969)

Holt, J. *General view of the agriculture of the county of Lancaster* (1795)

Hyde, F.E. *Liverpool and the Mersey* (Newton Abbot 1971)

Lewis, M.J.T. *Early wooden railways* (1970)

Rowse, A.L. *Bosworth Field and the Wars of the Roses* (1968)

Wadsworth, A.P. and Mann J. de L. *The cotton trade and industrial Lancashire, 1600-1780* (Manchester 1931)

Walker, A. *Tour of the Lake Counties* (1792)

Index